RESTORE

REMEMBERING LIFE'S HURTS WITH THE GOD WHO REBUILDS

A 7-SESSION BIBLE STUDY

SUSANNAH BAKER

© 2022 Susannah Baker

All rights reserved. No part of this publication may be reproduced, distributed, or transmitted in any form or by any means, including photocopying, recording, or other electronic or mechanical methods, without the prior written permission of the publisher, except in the case of brief quotations embodied in critical reviews and certain other noncommercial uses permitted by copyright law. For permission requests, contact the author through the link below.

Connect with me at susannahbaker.com/connect

First paperback edition: March, 2022
Published by Susannah Baker
SusannahBaker.com

Cover and book design by Sheila Parr
Cover image © Shutterstock / Oaurea

Unless otherwise noted, all Scripture quotations are taken from the ESV® Bible (The Holy Bible, English Standard Version®), copyright © 2001 by Crossway, a publishing ministry of Good News Publishers. Used by permission. All rights reserved. Scripture quotations taken from the (NASB®) New American Standard Bible®, Copyright © 1960, 1971, 1977, 1995 by The Lockman Foundation. Used by permission. All rights reserved. www.lockman.org. Scripture quotations marked MSG are taken from THE MESSAGE, copyright © 1993, 2002, 2018 by Eugene H. Peterson. Used by permission of NavPress, represented by Tyndale House Publishers. All rights reserved. Scripture quotations marked (NIV) are taken from the Holy Bible, New International Version®, NIV®. Copyright © 1973, 1978, 1984, 2011 by Biblica, Inc.® Used by permission of Zondervan. All rights reserved worldwide. www.zondervan.com The "NIV" and "New International Version" are trademarks registered in the United States Patent and Trademark Office by Biblica, Inc.®

ISBN: 978-1-7379589-3-2

CONTENTS

The Lord is my shepherd;
I shall not want.
He makes me lie down in green pastures.
He leads me beside still waters.
He RESTORES my soul.
He leads me in paths of righteousness
for his name's sake.
Even though I walk through the
valley of the shadow of death,
I will fear no evil,
for You are with me;
Your rod and Your staff,
they comfort me.
You prepare a table before me
in the presence of my enemies;
You anoint my head with oil;
my cup overflows.
Surely goodness and mercy
shall follow me
all the days of my life,
and I shall dwell in the house of the Lord
forever.

—Psalm 23:1–6

INTRODUCTION

Dear friend,

I've been where you are. I've been restless, anxious, and full of doubt that I would ever be able to change or that my life would ever be defined by anything but failure and regret.

But at my lowest point, God didn't wait for me to get it together, clean up my act, or become the perfect person He was hoping I would be. My failures are exactly where He met me. In fact, they were what He was waiting for. Our resources will never be sufficient, but God's are—He gives us His steadfast love, faithful presence, constant forgiveness, endless mercy, boundless confidence, and richest grace.

The journey of remembering my past and allowing God to restore and heal my soul was long, hard, and painful at times. But God's presence through His Spirit and His Word steadied my heart, secured my steps, and showed me my story through the lens of His redemption, hope, and grace.

This same journey is available to you as well.

Little by little, step by step, and day by day, through reading, praying, receiving the truth of God's Word, and trusting Him enough to obey, you will learn to see your story through His lens. You will learn to replace your doubt with trust, your sorrow with comfort, your fear with His unfailing love, and your deepest despair with peace. God's Word makes us strong in the broken places when we are willing to bring all of our brokenness to Him.

This study doesn't take the place of going to a counselor's office or seeing professionals or people with much more expertise, skill, and knowledge than I have, but it does offer a place to begin your journey towards healing every day for the next seven weeks—smack dab in the middle of God's Word.

The only prerequisite is that you come as you really are, willing to encounter the God who really is. He is your good Father who has set a table before you in the presence of your enemies as His securely beloved child.

Restoration is waiting.

Expectant for the journey ahead,

HOW TO USE THIS STUDY

PERSONAL STUDY

This seven-week Bible study was created to use alongside the book *Restore: Remembering Life's Hurts with the God Who Rebuilds* and guides you through the process of secure attachment. Each week has five days of Personal Study to help you dig into God's Word, along with prompts to guide you in the process of prayer as you learn to look up and out to your good heavenly Father.

To help with the healing process, on days when the questions become intense or remembering and processing just feels too hard, I have included a section after the times of closing prayer called "Continuing the Calm." These sections are written by Chelsea Rhoden, MA, CCTP, LPC Associate under the supervision of Erik Salwen, PhD, LPC-S, and Joy Sumrall, LPC-S. Chelsea has helped countless people process hard details from their stories with the grace and goodness of God. She supervises a trauma healing team that regularly works with women in the Middle East to help them remember, restore, and rebuild from some very hard places. Chelsea is not only a wise counselor, but she is also a guide you can trust in your own journey of restoration and rebuilding in the days ahead. You can find her at chelsearhoden.com, where she provides more exercises and tips on restoring and rebuilding from hard places.

For each day of Personal Study, you will need:

- your own personal copy of the book *Restore: Remembering Life's Hurts with the God Who Rebuilds*. Before you begin each week of Personal Study, you will be asked to read specific chapters in the book. Reading these chapters is essential to understanding and completing the Personal Study part of the workbook.
- a Bible in the English Standard Version (or access to a Bible website or app—www.biblegateway.com and the ESV Bible app are two of my favorites).
- your favorite pen to write in this book and in your Bible (if that is something you feel comfortable doing).
- approximately thirty minutes each day to complete the lesson.

VIDEO TEACHINGS

Each video teaching is available for free and can be accessed from my website, www.susannahbaker.com/biblestudies. A Viewer Guide is provided in the workbook at the beginning of each week to help you take notes as you watch.

Whether you're doing the study alone or with a group, you will watch each video session *before* completing the Personal Study for that week. I would encourage you to not skip out on watching the videos—each one will add to your understanding of how God's Word applies and guides us in the secure attachment process to the Lord.

LEADER GUIDE

In the back of this workbook is a leader guide with instructions on how to lead a group through each week of study. You will need approximately 60–80 minutes to complete each week's group session.

Each group session includes the following four sections:

Read

- A Scripture to read and pray through together before watching the video session

Watch

- A video teaching approximately 30 minutes in length

Discuss

- Questions to help the group process the Personal Study from each week
- Questions to help the group process the video teaching from each week

Pray

- Prompts to ask participants to share one prayer request each week that pertains to their own personal journey of restoration
- A Scripture to read and prompts to pray to close your group time together

Group Size

Your group could be a Bible study, Sunday school class, or any small group gathering. If you are using this workbook in a larger group setting, breaking up into circles of four to six participants for the discussion questions is ideal so each person has a chance to share, process, and heal in a smaller, safer setting. Please make sure you designate one person in each group to act as a facilitator during the times of discussion.

Materials Needed

Each group participant should have:

- Their own personal copy of this Bible study, as well as their own copy of the book *Restore: Remembering Life's Hurts with the God Who Rebuilds*. Each participant will be asked to read specific chapters in the book before beginning each week of Personal Study. Reading these chapters is essential to understanding and completing the personal study part of the workbook.
- A Bible in the English Standard Version

THE JOURNEY AHEAD

We all begin the process of restoration from different places with different backgrounds and stories. But we are all walking toward the same Father, who is running toward us. May the next seven weeks transform the way you see Him and help you have a deeper knowledge of the way He loves you as His child. Let the journey begin.

WEEK 1

The Need to Restore

VIEWER GUIDE: WEEK 1

THE JOURNEY AHEAD

PSALM 84:1–12

Three beatitudes, or blessings, give us unifying perspective, courage, and joy in our journey:

- Our ___Identity___ (Psalm 84:1–4)
    - In our journey, we are sojourners or ___pilgrims___, people who are not home yet but are ___on the way___.
    - As sojourners, we have to untangle our ___loyalties often___.
    - We are loyal to the ___person___ and presence of ___God___, to the ___family___ of God, and to our ___home___ with Him one day.
- Our ___Strength___ (Psalm 84:5–8)
    - On this journey, we go from one ___degree___ of strength to another (v. 7).
    - Our strength is found on the ___highways___ to ___Zion___.

- Restoration isn't the emphasis of our circumstances

* what stays unremembered, stays unhealed.

* joy isn't dependent on a set of circumstances

- In the Hebrew, the word *Zion* comes from a word meaning dryness, drought, parched ground, desert, dry waste.[1]
- To ascend the highway to Zion, we must descend, just as Jesus did.

Zion is a physical picture of His grace.

- Our goal (Psalm 84:9–12)
  - The psalmist isn't reward-resistant; he is running towards reward.

Video Sessions available at susannahbaker.com/biblestudies.

Raised Roads

- prayer
- songs
- community
- meditation of God's word

– You are the Beloved

– God doesn't call us to be "successful." He calls us to be fruitful.

PERSONAL STUDY

Before beginning this week's study, please read the introduction and chapters 1–4 of the book, *Restore: Remembering Life's Hurts with the God Who Rebuilds.*

DAY 1

Read

Today's Personal Study refers to chapter 1 of the book: "Remembering the Ruins."

Reflect

This most important thing to remember from today's chapter is this: attachment matters.

Every human being comes out of the womb wired for attachment, and if they do not securely attach to their primary caretaker, every other relationship in life will follow the same pattern of insecure attachment unless they do some serious heart work.

Refer to chapter one of the book. In the space provided, list the four basic ways children attach to their primary caretakers.

1) secure
2) insecure/avoidant
3) insecure/ambivalent
4) insecure/disorganized

Many of us had parents who loved us, yet still passed down to us their insecure patterns of attachment. Maybe it was the result of pain in their own past, lack of understanding, or lack of resources that kept them from moving forward on their journey toward healing and earned secure attachment.

Or, perhaps we grew up with a secure attachment to at least one of our primary caretakers until a traumatic or painful event—beyond their control—damaged that attachment. So, we slipped into an insecure pattern of attachment, a pattern that infiltrates and influences every other relationship in our life.

That's the bad news.

The good news is this: earned secure attachment is available for anyone who chooses to go on a journey with God.

Is this a journey God cares about and offers to every single one of His children through relationship to Jesus Christ? Absolutely. But I want you to see it for yourself.

Read Psalm 16:8–11. Fill in the blank from verse 9.

Therefore my heart is glad, and my whole being rejoices;
My flesh also dwells securely.

Right here, smack dab in the middle of our Bibles, is the word "secure." And it's not just in Psalm 16; it's everywhere throughout the Psalms.

When I started on my journey of understanding insecure attachment and moving toward a place of wholeness and healing, I was stunned: written within the pages of the book of Psalms was the language of earned secure attachment. The psalmists were real people—people who struggled with insecure attachment themselves. People who had relatively easy childhoods and people who had tough childhoods. People who experienced forced evacuations of their homelands, ethnic cleansings, persecution, famine, drought, the loss of loved ones, depression, despair, anguish, and anxiety but whose hearts were set on moving from a place of insecurity to the firm foundation of earned secure attachment with God.

For confirmation, let's take a look at one more passage in the Psalms: Psalm 40:1–3.

While we don't know the specifics of his circumstances, what we do know is that David, the writer of this psalm, was not in a great place. Where was David when he cried out to the Lord (v. 2)? -the pit of destruction

-the miry clay

Think for a moment about what the "pit of destruction" could be. List some ideas. Highlight the one that feels the most like a "pit of destruction" for you.

• depression • feeling useless/purposeless • health concerns

• anxiety • financial struggle • prodigal children

What did God do for David? Specifically, what did David say God did for his "steps"? Which of these things do you most need? Why?

• He set my feet on a rock - making my footsteps firm.

As David moved from an insecure to a secure place (v. 3), what happened to the people around him? Why is this important?

many will see & fear the Lord

& will trust in the Lord

- God wants to turn our misery into ministry.

We spend so much of our time and energy trying to change the people around us: our spouse, our children, our extended family, neighbors, co-workers, and friends. But rest assured of something profound Scripture affirms: as you begin to change, the people closest to you will begin to change. As you begin to move to a place of security, so will your spouse, your children, your family, and your friends.

The good news today is that even if you are insecurely attached, secure attachment is available for you and for the people you love as you trust the Lord and keep your steps and your gaze firmly fixed on Him.

Respond

Father,

In a world that is unstable and has many ups and downs, my heart craves a life of security and stability. Thank You for the promise that as I cry out and wait for You, You will deliver me. You will steady my heart and make my steps secure. Help me to wait on You for the deliverance You promise to provide.

Continuing the Calm

In preparation for the coming weeks, begin thinking about ways you might find additional peace and support. There's a good chance that doing the hard work on these pages will bring up some emotions that continue long after you put the book down and walk away. The goal is to guide you to a place of peace with your heavenly Father. Sometimes this takes a little more time, focus, and support than we might expect. Take a few minutes to jot down three to four things that might help you if you find yourself stuck in a low place. It might be quiet music. Maybe you have a favorite Scripture you can think on and pray to the Lord. Perhaps there's a friend you could call or a calming activity you could do.

Consider this your emergency list. It's to help you remember what to do when you need it.

- worship music
- a good podcast
- Bible study

DAY 2

Read

Today's Personal Study refers to pages 23–32 in chapter 2 of the book, "Understanding Attachment Styles," ending with the section "Children with Insecure-Disorganized Attachment."

Reflect

Understanding attachment styles and how they play out in real life is relatively easy. But understanding your own attachment style and identifying the patterns of reacting and distancing that your attachment style has caused can be difficult. It is painful to look honestly at the ways we often deal with the people we love and admit our failures and shortcomings.

But the first step toward healing is to understand and admit who you really are, not the person you wish you were or pretend to be. And this isn't just psychological jargon—this is a biblical mandate for anyone who wants to grow, change, and heal.

Read Psalm 32:1–7.

What happened to David when he kept silent about his sin (vv. 3–4)? When have you seen this happen in your own life? • my body wasted away

• my vitality is drained away

• I have been Physically sick in my sin!

How did forgiveness, healing, and growth come to David (v. 5)? Why do you think it's often so difficult for us to follow David's example?

- He acknowledged his sin to God
- He did not hide his iniquity
- He confessed to Lord

→ It's hard to admit!

David was his own worst enemy. When he hid his sin from God, others, and perhaps even himself, he wasted away and was dying. But when he confessed his sin to God, he received mercy. Forgiveness. Grace. Instead of distancing and being his own hiding place, he finally made God his hiding place (v. 7)—and that is when his restoration began.

What about you? Are you willing to be honest about where you really are today and what you might be hiding within? If so, then the journey toward earned secure attachment can begin. We start by understanding our attachment pattern with our primary caretakers because it's helpful to start by looking at our behavior now and then trace it back to its beginnings.

Look back at the sections in chapter two of the book under "Attachment in Children." After reading through the ways children in the Strange Situation reacted or responded to their parents, which description resonated with you the most? Why?

Insecure/avoidant — I felt that my mom couldn't handle any of my emotions so I gave her none!

How does that attachment pattern or behavior relate to the way you interacted with your primary caretakers?

I was self-reliant

Now think about your relationship with your parents or primary caretakers today or in the recent past. What dynamics in your relationship might make sense now that you understand a little bit more about attachment patterns? Explain.

My parents went through something very traumatic... I learned to self-rely so as not to bring stress on them. I still do that to this day!

Now, I know what many of you are probably thinking: You are hesitant to dig too deep into the relational dynamic with your parents because you love your parents and want to assure yourself and others that you had "good parents." I understand. I felt, and still do feel, the same way about my own parents. I have great parents, good parents, godly parents. But they were not perfect parents. No parents are. And as a parent myself, I bring my own set of issues, failures, and frustrations to my own daughters.

But staying stuck in the past means being unwilling to admit honestly what your past was like. In fact, being unwilling to be honest about your relationship with your parents is a hindrance to healing—not only to your own healing but to theirs as well.

Whatever sin is unconfessed stays in the dark. And whatever is in the dark maintains control over us. Only when we honestly admit who we are, who other people are, and what really happened to us in the past, are we free then to forgive, step into the light, and break the hold darkness has on us.

The kindest and most gracious thing you can do for your parents is admit what your relationship with them was really like so you can truly forgive; fully release them from any debt they might owe; turn your eyes to Jesus; and begin to heal, change, and grow. Remember, when you change, you give your parents the freedom, space, and permission to change as well. It's a win-win situation.

So, let's start by being honest. In your own words, describe your attachment style with your parents based on what you have read so far in the book.

We will spend more time on this when we work through the chapters on remembrance, but do you need to begin the process of forgiving your parents or primary caretakers today—either for things they did do, didn't do, or perhaps were incapable of doing because of pain, hurt, trauma, or lack of resources from their own past and insecure attachment patterns? If so, take a moment to write out a prayer of forgiveness, and tell the Lord you want to begin the journey of setting them free so you can be free too.

God help me to forgive my mom who was+ is carrying so much pain from all the trauma in her life.

Now write out a prayer asking the Lord to fill with His love every space that needs filling because of a parent's lack. Ask that as He fills you, you will be able to give that love freely and generously to the people around you, beginning with your parents or caretakers. (If one or both of your parents is deceased, or you are not able to be in active relationship with your parents, that is okay. You are still able to forgive them and allow the love of the Lord to begin to change your memories of and feelings toward your parents. As you release your situation to Him and trust His love, He will begin to change your heart.)

God help me to rely on you & not hold a grudge against my mom - she did the best she could & she's so swe

Well done. I know that might have been difficult for some of you. Remember, healing is a journey accomplished one day, one step at a time. I am proud of you for taking a hard first step on the path of honesty and forgiveness.

Respond

Father,
Understanding and remembering the roots of my attachment pattern is hard work. But there is never a place You ask me to go where Your presence does not lead me and stay by my side. Help me lean on your wisdom, truth, and grace for every step of journey—even when the steps are hard.

DAY 3

Read

Today's Personal Study refers to pages 32–42 in chapter 2 of the book, "Understanding Attachment Styles," beginning with the section "Attachment in Adults."

Reflect

Like we talked about yesterday, understanding attachment styles and how they play out in real life is relatively easy. But owning and identifying the patterns of reacting and distancing that your own attachment style has caused is difficult. It's never easy to take an honest and intentional look at the ways we deal with the people we love most.

Total transparency before God is psychologically the safest place to be. When we confess our sin before Him, He becomes our hiding place and surrounds us with songs of deliverance (Psalm 32:7). This is when He puts "a new song in [our] mouth, a song of praise to our God" (Psalm 40:3), and those who hear it and see the difference in our lives will place their trust in God as well.

Since it can be difficult to look honestly at our past and patterns of attachment with our parents, sometimes it helps to start by looking at our behavior in the present.

Dr. Gregg Jantz created four questions to help you think about your behavior in the present to determine your attachment style from the past:

- Am I worthy of being loved?
- Am I able to do what I need to do to get the love I need?
- Are other people reliable and trustworthy?
- Are other people accessible and willing to respond to me when I need them?[2]

The way you answer these questions can clue you in about your attachment pattern. Look back in the book at the pages you read for today and look over the answers someone with each style of attachment usually gives to those four questions.

Circle which set of answers resonates with you the most from the following list.

- Secure Attachment
- Insecure-Avoidant Attachment
- Insecure-Ambivalent Attachment
- Insecure-Disorganized Attachment

Now, write out the answers to the four questions for that attachment style.

Perhaps the fact that you identify with or believe a certain set of answers to those questions doesn't surprise you. But what surprised me—and might surprise you—about attachment theory was why I believed the answers.

I already knew I was insecure. I already knew I was always afraid others would abandon me or that my needs would not be met. I already knew I was too needy or too angry much of the time. I already knew I struggled with feeling like I had to work hard to secure other people's love and approval. I just thought there was something uniquely and deeply wrong with me. I thought I was worse than everyone else and that no matter how hard I worked to change, I couldn't. I'd been trapped in an endless cycle of insecurity for years.

But then I realized the source of so much of my insecurity: my attachment pattern.

I am not saying this to place undue blame on my parents or to somehow suggest my own sin issues of anger and insecurity were not my fault—I was fully responsible for my own sin. But I suddenly held the keys to understanding the cycle I was trapped in and to digging out of the pit I kept falling into.

Instead of blaming or relying on my parents to change and waiting for people around me to stabilize, I could choose to change by placing all my security and trust in the Lord and waiting for Him to deliver me. I could choose to believe and act on the fact that God Himself is my primary caretaker, and in His hands, my past, present, and future are stable and secure.

Friends, this is freedom. This was the best news I had heard in years. This meant all my efforts and energy could go into making the Lord my safe place, not other people. This meant I could take the pressure off my parents, my family, and my friends to be what I needed when I needed them and learn to rely on the only One who could ever fulfill my deepest needs.

I didn't need to keep hiding my sin or beating myself up for my failures—I needed to recognize that the secure person and place I had been searching for throughout my life was ready and waiting for me to depend on Him. All I had to do was learn how to take His hand, trust His touch, and receive His love on my good days and hard days alike.

Let's close today on a hopeful note by reading Psalm 25:8–10.

Who does God instruct? Perfect people? People with pure pasts and faultless pedigrees? (Hint: Look closely at verse 8.)

Sinners

Name the prerequisite for learning from God a new way and new path to walk (vv. 9–10)?

humility

As we learn to follow the Lord and securely attach to Him, what is the assurance He gives us (v. 10)?

all the paths of the Lord are lovingkindness & truth

Hear me on this: it is never too late to start following the Lord. It is never too late to start the journey of healing from insecure attachment and moving toward to secure attachment. All it requires is a heart that's willing to walk a new path of humble dependence on Him.

Respond

Father,
Looking honestly at my past requires courage and humility. I ask for both as I continue to walk the path of healing ahead. Don't let me stay stuck in the pit of blame or unforgiveness, but help me to own my faults and sin, and choose a new way of relating to you, my parents, and those around me, a way that comes from being secure in Your love.

DAY 4

Read

Today's study refers to chapter 3 of the book: "Why We Remember Rightly."

Reflect

As we begin our journey of restoration and moving toward earned secure attachment, we must begin by remembering.

I'll be honest with you: remembering hurts. To remember, some of us will have to return to some pretty painful places. Places where our unhealed selves and unresolved hurt caused a lot of hurt in other people's lives. Places where other people unjustly caused a lot of hurt in our own lives too.

And for that hurt, I am so sorry. If there was any other way for restoration to occur apart from remembering, I would gladly offer it to you. But I have to tell you the truth: unless we choose to remember our past, even the painful parts, what remains buried will maintain control over us. Only what is unremembered can remain unhealed. And only what is unremembered can stand block or hinder us from receiving the deep-down-healing, life-changing, soul-freeing love of God.

But Miroslav Volf reminds us that "it is important not merely to remember, but also to remember *rightly*."[3]

Before I began to walk down the road of restoration, I didn't understand that there were two ways to remember. We can remember our past and suffering through the lens of our own sin, despair, anxiety, and dread, apart from the grace of God, or we can remember our past and others' betrayal through the steadfast love and faithfulness of the Lord, even in our most painful places. How we remember is as essential as what we remember.

No one has taught me more about remembering rightly than David—Old Testament shepherd, warrior, psalmist, and king. Despite David's title as a "man after [God's] own heart" (1 Samuel 13:14) he had many terrible and appalling things happen to him. Just because someone is chosen and anointed by God doesn't mean they are immune to suffering. In fact, some of God's greatest chosen instruments experience greater or more intense suffering than anyone else. While I do not pretend to know or understand all God's reasons for allowing suffering in the lives of the people He loves, I do know "while sin always blocks our relationship with God, suffering can deepen it."[4] Suffering is often what keeps us close to God, dependent, needy, and in turn, more reliant on a continual supply of His supernatural power, security, strength, and love.

Read Psalm 143:3–6.

Describe the condition of David's heart by using clues from his words in verses 3–4.

- persecuted - crushed - dwell in dark places
- overwhelmed
- appalled

When David found himself in a pit of darkness, despair, and trauma, what did he do? Specifically, what did he remember, meditate on, and ponder? How does this teach us to respond when we experience darkness, despair, or trauma?

- I remember the days of old
- I meditate on all your doings
- I muse on the works of your hands

Who or what did he stretch out his hands to and why (v. 6)?

to you ... my soul longs for you as in a parched land.

Even in David's darkest moments, when he was looking for rescue, relief, and healing, he didn't first demand God to act on his behalf (although he did so later in the psalm), he first drew near to God through remembrance. He stretched out his hands to God Himself—not a quick solution or ten-step program, but to the presence of God who is active, alive, and personally involved in His life.

As Derek Kidner writes, David "reaches out towards God himself, not only to the things he can be asked to do. It is this personal devotion [to God] that was David's greatness . . . and is the continuing greatness of his psalms."[5] This movement toward the person and presence of God—no matter the memories or the circumstances—can become your and my personal greatness as well. God's presence actively involved in our lives can become what defines us rather than bondage to a painful past.

When life is dark and your memories are painful, don't start with meditating on the memory. Start with meditating on God. Remember His power, His presence, His promises, His life, and then ask Him to help you remember all your past, even the painful parts, through the reality of that lens.

Take a look at Psalm 25:10.

All the paths of the Lord are steadfast love and faithfulness,
for those who keep His covenant and His testimonies.

Circle how many paths of the Lord are defined by His steadfast love and faithfulness, then put a box around the two ways those paths are defined.

Now read Psalm 26:2–3 in your Bible. Along with Psalm 25:10, these two verses didn't just become a hope and a prayer during my most intense days of remembering and healing—they also became a determined battle cry.

I think they are vital in your journey of healing as well. I want you to write them out word-for-word in the space below.

By the time I turned forty, I was tired of remembering my past through the lens of rejection. I was tired of walking through every day in a fog of despair. I wanted to learn how to take God at His Word and start remembering, thinking, believing, and reminding myself that "all" God's paths were steadfast love and faithfulness. The things I regretted about my past, the things I felt so much shame and self-hatred over, the relationships I felt so insecure in, I could learn to see differently—I could learn to see them through the lens of God's steadfast love and faithfulness.

It was a choice, I tell you. It was a choice to set my alarm, get up early, and immerse myself in His Word—to let the lens of who God really was and what He was truly capable of change how I thought about my past, present, and future. It was a choice to learn to offer grace to myself and, ultimately, grace to others as I began to see things in a whole new light. But through those choices and God's radical love and grace, each choice became one small step closer to earned secure attachment and discarding my old lens.

Friends, remembering our past through the lens of God's steadfast love and faithfulness changes us and shapes us so we can step boldly and confidently into our present and future.

So, are you ready? Are you ready to learn how to see your entire life through the lens of God's grace and goodness instead of human sin and devastation? I hope so. Because when you do, restoration rushes in on the heels of right remembering. Get ready.

Respond

Father,

All Your paths are steadfast love and faithfulness (Psalm 25:10). All of them. But I confess I remember so much of my life through a lens of despair and darkness. I remember feeling like You were nowhere near when I needed You the most. Help me, Lord. Like David, help me to stretch out my hands to You; to remember Your character, Your ways, and the works You have done so I can remember my past and live out my present and future rightly—through the lens of Your steadfast love.

DAY 5

Read

Today's study refers to chapter 4 of the book: "What We Remember and Why."

Reflect

There are two primary things we are called, throughout Scripture, to remember as believers:

1. God's saving acts in world history
2. God's saving acts in our own personal history

Next week, we will start the process of remembering specific details from our own personal history so we can be free to walk into a healed, secure, and restored present and future. But today I want to spend time thinking about God's saving acts in world history.

Many of us have probably read or even heard about some of God's most famous or notable saving acts—parting the Red Sea, delivering the Israelites from Egyptian slavery, causing the walls of Jericho to come tumbling down, or rescuing Daniel from certain death in the lions' den. But what we don't often remember is that every saving act of God flows from the character of God.

Today I want to spend some time meditating on the character of God that is behind each and every one of His saving acts in world history and in our own personal history so we are ready for our work of remembering next week.

Read Exodus 33:18–23.

Describe Moses's request to the Lord (v. 18). When have you made a similar request to God?

- Now show me your glory
- in the infertility crisis

How did the Lord tell Moses He would answer his request (v. 19)? What would He cause to pass in front of Moses, and what would He proclaim?

I will cause my glory to pass in front of you / I will proclaim my name.

What we learn from these verses is that God's glory is His goodness, and the way we access that goodness is through knowing His name. God's name isn't just a title; it's a promise to act and move in our lives in a way that consistently brings glory to Him and goodness to us.

When you think of God's name, is that what you think of? Goodness? Love? Grace and Mercy? Or do you think things like: Harsh. Remote. Distant. Disapproving. Disappointed. Be as honest as you possibly can. List the first two characteristics that come into your head and heart when you think about God.

- Good
- Sovereign

If I'm honest with myself, I often think of negative things in relation to God's presence, name, or activity in my life. But the more I press into healing, restoration, and remembering, the more I have to confront my real beliefs about who God is—not just my professed beliefs—and replace them with the truth when necessary.

So, what is the truth about who God is and how He acts and moves in our lives?

Keep reading in Exodus 34:6–8.

As Dane Ortlund writes about this passage in Exodus in his book, *Gentle and Lowly*, "Short of the incarnation itself, this is perhaps the high point of divine revelation in all the Bible."[6] One key indicator of this passage's importance is how many times we see it quoted and used in other places throughout the Old Testament. Let's dive in and see what makes these verses so significant.

What are the first two characteristics God used to define Himself (v. 6)?

compassionate & gracious God

Look back at the ways you most often think of God. Does it line up with those first two characteristics?

–No!
–God give me more compassion!

Now look at the next set of characteristics God used to describe Himself. Fill in the blanks below.

"slow to ___anger___ and abounding in steadfast ___love___ and ___faithfulness___."

Again, be honest with yourself: Is this how you most often think about God? Is this how you would describe Him? Explain.

– I do think about God being gracious!

I don't know about you, but even after years of being a Christian, I have to work hard against my natural thoughts and assumptions about God so I don't think about God as "quick to anger," "ready to punish," "abounding in disappointment," and "always overflowing with wrath." We naturally tend to think wrong thoughts about God. This is because Satan is no dummy. He knows that if we think God is distant, disapproving, and punishing, then we will stay far away from Him. We will profess with our lips that we love Him but keep our hearts protected from full faith, trust, and surrender. After all, who wants to get too close to a perpetually angry God? That's why, as Ortlund writes:

> The Christian life, from one angle, is the long journey of letting our natural assumption about who God is, over many decades, fall away, being slowly replaced with God's own insistence on who he is. This is hard work. It takes a lot of sermon and a lot of suffering to believe that God's deepest heart is "merciful and gracious, slow to anger." . . . Perhaps Satan's greatest victory in your life today is not the sin in which you regularly indulge but the dark thoughts of God's heart that cause you to go there in the first place and keep you cool towards him in the wake of it.[7]

Hear me on this: you are not alone in your fight to think right thoughts about God. I am right there with you. But friends, we must do the hard work of examining who God tells us He really is, replacing the lies we have believed about Him for so long with the truth. Our restoration, wholeheartedness, and secure attachment depends on it.

Look one last time at Exodus 34:7.

How many people and generations does He keep steadfast love and extend forgiveness to? thousands

In contrast, how many generations does He visit iniquity on?

children & their children to the 3rd & 4th generation

The contrast is startling, isn't it? To be just and good, does God have to punish sin? Does He have to dole out just consequences to those who deserve them? Yes, but His steadfast love and forgiveness far surpass His wrath. To put it another way, "God's goodness will be passed down in a way that inexorably swallows up all our sins."[8]

To finish today and this week, I want us to look one last place in Scripture.

Read Psalm 50:21.

What is God's rebuke and charge to His people?

You thought I was exactly like you

Before we enter the hard and painful work of remembering our own personal histories, we must remember this: God is not like us. He is not like me: quick to wrath, offense, and holding tightly onto grudges. He is merciful and gracious, slow to anger, and abounding in love. Everything God does and allows to happen in our lives is rooted in His unchanging goodness, glory, and grace. Our job is to take Him at His word and learn to trust Him as He really is.

Respond

Father,

It is hard work to take off the lens of my false assumptions about who You are and put on the truth of Your goodness and glory. As I read about Your saving acts in world history throughout Scripture, help me remember that every single one of Your acts is a good and glorious display of who You are. As I prepare to remember my own personal history, teach me to remember my life through the lens of Your unchanging mercy, grace, and abounding steadfast love.

Continuing the Calm

The attributes of God are proof that He is our refuge and safe place. It's easy to notice them and move on quickly through our study of the Bible. When you have a few extra minutes, think of some of the Lord's attributes that draw out your affections for Him.

If you can't think of any attributes of God right away, look at the following list for help. God is:

- Eternal
- Merciful
- Good
- Grace-giving
- Ever-Present
- Unchanging
- Active
- Holy
- Just
- Sovereign
- Loving
- Self-Existent
- Transcendent (Beyond Our Understanding)
- Righteous
- All-Knowing
- All-Powerful[9]

Sit quietly before the Lord and praise Him for these things. Spend extra time here worshiping Him, enjoying His nearness.

You may begin with a small list of things you appreciate about God, but as you bring your focus to this quiet place of worship, your heart and your mind will change. Research shows some remarkable things about the way worship changes the body as well, all of which goes to show that we are made to worship God.

This is a safe, good, healing place. Remember this as one of the places to run to when the work gets tough and you find yourself stuck and feeling low. Some counselors might call this "a coping skill," but as David knew, running to God is the coping skill. It is the best and only way to move toward full healing. Practice meeting the Lord a few minutes a day in full adoration, appreciation, and praise. The more you practice, the more you'll find yourself drawn to this time with God, and the more you'll look for Him in every situation.

WEEK 2

How We Remember

HOW GOD HELPS US REMEMBER

THE QUESTIONS (GENESIS 3:1–13)

- Through His wise and discerning questions, God encourages Adam and Eve to tell Him exactly:
  - where they are
  - why they are hiding
  - what they have done
  - the lies they believe about God and themselves
  - where the lies come from
- God's questions:
  - bring the dark places of our hearts into the light so that we can be forgiven, healed, and restored.
  - invite us to make God our hiding place.
  - make us pay attention to the lies we believe and who we are listening to.
  - draw out not only where we are but also why we are there.
  - let us know He has not left us on our own but is looking for us.
  - show His desire to access our hearts.

—the blood of Jesus forgives sin.
—the water of the word cleanses us from shame.
Ephesians

THE RESPONSE (GENESIS 3:14–24)

- God gives consequences because He is just (vv. 14–19, 22–24).
- He gives covering because He is merciful (v. 21).
- Even in consequences, He gives hope (vv. 15, 21).
  - We remember as a people already on their way to resurrection life / deliverance.

* We remember in a way that leads to life, not death.

THE CHOICE

- We can spend the rest of our lives:
  - hiding, choosing not to remember and being held hostage by the past and its pain.
  - Remembering destructively through the lens of bitterness, wrongs suffered, and lies we believe about the character of God.
  - Remembering rightly through the blessing of our covering, relationship with the Son, and the hope of our deliverance to come.
  - This one choice will affect everything.

insecure/avoidant: your tendency is to hide.

Video Sessions available at susannahbaker.com/biblestudies.

* Sin & shame separates us from God
* suffering pushes us to God.

PERSONAL STUDY

Before beginning this week's study, please read chapters 5–6 of the book.

DAY 1

Read

Today's Personal Study refers to chapter 5 of the book: "How We Remember."

Reflect

In last week's study, we established that in the journey of moving toward earned secure attachment, we must do the hard but good work of remembering. And as we remember, we must remember two things: God's saving acts in world history and God's saving acts in our own personal history.

In our own personal histories, we must remember our parents or primary caretakers and the ways we securely or insecurely attached to them those first few years of life. We must remember how that pattern of attachment has played out in every other relationship in our lives and look honestly at the hurt, pain, or damage done to us or by us. And then we must invite Jesus into those memories, learn to see them through His lens, release and forgive those who have held us captive through bitterness, unforgiveness, and pain, and continue the journey of securely attaching to God as our heavenly Father.

But like we talked about last week, before we try to remember our personal histories, we must turn our eyes up and out to see the beauty, truth, goodness, holiness, justice, and righteousness of God Himself first. This is how we begin to remember—we first look at God.

Many of our personal histories contain hard, dark, and ugly things. If healing requires remembering, we must first learn to trust the One we are inviting into that history. Learning to trust the goodness and character of God enough to invite Him into our most personal moments and memories can take a long time. But we can learn how to begin that process of building trust gradually, step-by-step, day-by-day, memory-by-memory.

Read Psalm 16:8–11.

When David chose to set the Lord before Him and process his life—past, present, and future—in the presence of His good Father (vv. 8–9)—describe what happens to his . . .

- Heart: glad
- Whole being: rejoices
- Flesh: dwell securely

What did David say God would not do (v. 10)?

abandon His soul to Sheol

Before we embark on the journey of remembering, many of us need to hear this loud and clear: God will not abandon you.

Some of you had parents who left and abandoned you at a point in life when you needed them most. Maybe they abandoned you because of an affair or an addiction. Maybe they abandoned you because they were consumed by pain from their own past, and they lacked time, resources, will, or strength to deal with that pain. Maybe they abandoned you by dying of sickness, illness, accident, or old age—the last thing they wanted to do was to leave you, but because of the curse of sin and the weakness of their humanity, they were powerless against the enemy of death.

But God is not like our parents, either in their sin or in their human weakness. He is perfect and holy, never making promises He cannot keep. He is a good and ever-faithful Father who always stays and holds the power of life and death in His hands. Yes, each of us must take one final breath here on this earth one day, but because of the resurrection, we will rise to new life and live forever with Him one day.

Look back at Psalm 16. **What was the result of God's presence in David's life (v. 11)? (Hint: the right hand is a position of submission to God's power and authority.)**

fullness of joy -
pleasures evermore

When we think about remembering the hard things in our lives and inviting God into those memories, we need to know we are promised an abundance of life, not a lack of it. We a secure and stable path instead a life characterized by the fear that the rug will be pulled out from under us. And we are promised the protection and provision of His presence—we don't have to live in fear of or dread abandonment anymore. This doesn't mean we won't have to go to some hard places, but it does mean He will be with us every step of the way.

Look at Psalm 23:1–4 (NASB).

The Lord is my shepherd,
I will not be in need.
He lets me lie down in green pastures;
He leads me beside quiet waters.
He restores my soul;
He guides me in the paths of righteousness
For the sake of His name.
Even though I walk through the valley of the shadow of death,
I fear no evil, for You are with me;
Your rod and Your staff, they comfort me.

Circle the word "restores" in verse 3 and then underline what God promised to restore.

Circle the word "walk" in verse 4 and then underline where David walked.

Now watch carefully what happened in the journey of restoration.

- In verse 1, put a box around the words "The Lord."
- In verses 2–4, put a box around every pronoun that refers to the Lord.

As we begin the journey of restoration, we must remember what God promises to restore: our souls. We must be so careful to remember, God does not promise us restored circumstances in the here and now—that restoration will come one day when we live with Him forever in our forever home. But we are promised restored souls and renewed hearts in the present.

But when the journey gets the darkest, when the grief gets the thickest, when the valley grows the deepest—His presence becomes incarnational. When speaking of his own valley, David shifted from "He is with me" to "You are with me." This change in language just goes to show how deeply personal David's relationship with God was. While David didn't walk with God in the flesh, he experienced the peace of His presence through His Spirit and pointed us forward to Jesus, the Great Shepherd of the sheep. He did what no one else could so that we could experience God's presence in a completely different way. He can take us where no other guides can go because He went where no other person has gone—he went to the gates of hell, the deepest valley of the shadow. Because He lived a sinless life, the gates couldn't hold Him. He rushed up in resurrection life to the other side of death, taking with Him all other captives to sin who profess Him as Lord and believe in His name.

This is our promise as we remember: yes, we will have to trudge through the valley of death, but Jesus will be with us every step of the way. And in the process, He will restore our souls and give us resurrection life in the place of our darkest despair.

Respond

Father,

It is hard work to remember, but as we remember with Jesus by our side, we are promised the constancy of His presence, the restoration of our souls, and overflowing, abundant, resurrection life. Remind us of this in our darkest moments and give us strength for the journey ahead.

Continuing the Calm

The Lord is with you. This can sometimes be hard to fully grasp because we can't see Him physically. I want to invite you to close your eyes. Imagine a place that is calm or peaceful for you. It can be real or imagined. Notice the colors, the sounds, the smells, and the textures in this place. Spend time really building it up in your mind. Once you have spent time noticing the details, ask the Lord if He would come sit with you there. You don't have to know every detail about His face but imagine what it would be like to sit, rest, and talk with Him.

This kind of exercise may be new to you, or it may be something you already practice. When you have the Holy Spirit, He is with you wherever you go. Come here any time the outside world is chaotic and be present with the One who brings peace.

DAY 2

Read

Today's Personal Study refers to chapter 5 of the book: "How We Remember."

Reflect

Before we begin to dive into the details of our personal histories, I want to spend today reflecting on one more aspect of the lens through which the eyes of our hearts must learn to see our memories and personal histories: the lens of God's saving acts in world history. We have spent time talking about God's character, beginning to build a foundation of trust that God is a father and primary caretaker we can trust. But along with His character, we must learn to identify and remember the pattern and primary way He acts in the lives of His children.

While God delivered His people many times in many ways throughout the Old and New Testaments, there are two primary acts of deliverance that establish the pattern for every other act of deliverance God not only did in the past but also will do in the future.

The first one we'll look at is found in Psalm 78. This psalm was written to keep the people of Israel from forgetting about God's saving acts in their history as the people of God.

Read Psalm 78:1–7, 42–54.

In these opening verses, the psalmist explained why it's so important that God's people remember God's saving acts and tell their children the "things that we have heard and known, that our fathers have told us" (v. 3).

Look carefully at verse 7. Why is it so important that we remember God's saving acts? What does it help the people of God do?

to put our confidence in God & not forget His works

In verses 42–54, the psalmist described God's ultimate saving act on behalf of His people in the Old Testament. Skim through these verses and sum up in one word the event the psalmist pointed to and write it in the blank.

The Exodus

In just thirteen verses, the author of Psalm 78 summed up the entire event of the exodus—one that took Moses forty chapters to tell. God rescued His people from slavery, judged the false Egyptian gods through the ten plagues, led His people out of Egypt through the parting the Red Sea, decimated their enemies, and guided them to safety, to His "holy land" (Psalm 78:54).

In verse 55, we see an essential part of God's pattern of deliverance. What did He do for His people?

- drove out the nations before them
- apportioned for them an inheritance by measurement - made them dwell in tents

Now look back at Psalm 78:5–6. When the Israelites obeyed God's command to "remember" His saving acts in their personal history and tell them to their children and the next generation, what specific things would they have to remember, process, and tell? Circle everything below that is included.

- Memories of slavery
- Memories of suffering
- Memories of hardship and pain
- Memories of deprivation
- Memories of plagues and signs of judgment
- Memories of death
- Memories of being afraid
- Memories of a midnight rescue
- Memories of the miraculous
- Memories of deliverance
- Memories of safety
- Memories of protection
- Memories of provision
- Memories of settling into a new identity
- Memories of settling into a new place
- Memories of learning to be a new and different kind of people
- Memories of worshipping and serving a great, powerful, good, holy, trustworthy God

Here is where we so often get stuck. We want to move forward in our future. We want to forget and let the past be the past. But there is no movement forward without remembering both the good and the very hard things about the past. We cannot heal and remember our new identity, new name, new possibilities, new freedom, and a new way to look at our life-story unless we remember why we needed those things in the first place.

What makes the difference is how we remember the hard things. Do we remember the events of our slavery, hardship, and pain isolated from the deliverance and goodness of God? Or do we learn to remember them rightly, with the provision, protection, and miraculous acts of God integrated into them?

The second primary saving act of God we'll look at is the most important one. Read Ephesians 2:1–10.

What act of deliverance was the apostle Paul describing here?

In these ten verses, Paul summed up the greatest act of deliverance this world has ever seen. God rescues His people from slavery to sin; judges the "prince of the air" and all deeds done in our flesh (Ephesians 2:2–3); leads His people out of death to life through the cross and resurrection; decimates our enemies who would keep us from relationship and eternal life with Him; and guides us to safety, to "the immeasurable riches of his grace in kindness toward us in Christ Jesus" (Ephesians 2:7).

In verse 10, we see another essential part of God's pattern of deliverance. What happens to us once we have been rescued?

To learn how to remember rightly, as Miroslav Volf writes, "We need to place those memories into the framework of the sacred memory of the Exodus and Passion,"[10] which is the cross and resurrection of Christ. Both events preach to our hearts and minds, reminding us again and again that even on our darkest days, as the people of God, we remember as those who are "already on their way to deliverance."[11] What God did once, He will do again. And as Romans 8:32 says, "He who did not spare his own Son but gave him up for us all, how will he not also with him graciously give us all things?"

As we learn to remember with a God who saves, delivers, and acts on behalf of people at the center of our memories, the wrongs, pain, and hurts we have suffered are not the most defining events of our lives anymore. "Instead of being defined by how human beings relate to us, we are defined by how *God* relates to us. . . . We remember wrongs suffered as people with identities defined by God, not by wrongdoers' evil deeds and their echo in our memory. True, sometimes that echo is so powerful that it drowns out all other voices. Still, behind the unbearable noise of wrongdoing suffered, we can hear in faith the divinely composed music of our true identity."[12]

This is what God's two primary saving acts in world history—the exodus and the passion—teach us. We don't just remember the pain; we remember what He has brought us to. And what He brings us to is glorious.

Reread Ephesians 2:1–10.

What was your identity before God intervened (vv. 1–3)?

But through the great rescue of the cross of Christ, where has He called us to (vv. 4–6)?

What has He prepared in advance for us to do (v. 10)? Why is this important for us to understand?

- good works
- we have a purpose

Tomorrow we will start to remember specifics from our personal histories. But before we do, I want you to remember something now. We are a people who remember in hope. The past isn't meant to define us or confine us; it is meant to heal us and push us into our new identity and new possibilities that inevitably come to those who are the children of God. Everything in our past may not be good, but as we remember with God at the center, He will use it all for good—a goodness that is promised, secured, and already on its way. It's a goodness we see played out in the exodus and passion, promised to be passed down in the life of every person enslaved by sin who calls on the name of the Lord Jesus Christ to be saved. Resurrection and restoration are coming.

Respond

Father,

As I prepare to remember my past, I ask that You enlighten the eyes of my heart so that in every dark place, I would know the hope You have called me to, what are the riches of my glorious inheritance in the saints, and what is the immeasurable greatness of Your power toward those of us who believe (Ephesians 1:18–19). Because You demonstrated this power in the past by parting the seas and raising Christ from the dead, I trust You will do it again, not only for my heart in the here and now but also for my circumstances one day in my heavenly home.

DAY 3

Read

Today's Personal Study refers to chapter 6 of the book: "Remembering in the Storms."

Reflect

Today I want you to do some remembering. But as you remember, you can't forget: God wants to use your remembering to free you from being held as a prisoner to the pain of your past. He wants you to see all of your life—not just the good or easy parts, but the difficult and painful parts too—through the lens of His restorative goodness, presence, and grace. And He wants you to live out your new identity as His son or daughter, doing the good works He prepared in advance for you to do (Ephesians 2:10). Are you ready?

Let's get started.

To help you process today and tomorrow, please see the worksheet at the back of the book called, "Remembering Your Attachment."

Look back at Day Two from last week, specifically at what attachment style you most identified with. Circle your answer here, and then write your answer on the worksheet.

- Secure Attachment
- Insecure-Avoidant Attachment
- Insecure-Ambivalent Attachment
- Insecure-Disorganized Attachment

No matter what your attachment style might be, think of three words that most often describe your relationship with your mom or primary caretaker, and then write those words in the circles on the worksheet.

Now consider the memories or events that led to you using those words. In the chart on the following page, identify defining moments or memories that could have contributed to that description with your mom for each life stage. Don't overthink it; just write a brief description for the things that come to your mind and heart. I have provided more space for the early years since those usually define our attachment style.

AGE	MEMORY	HOW IT AFFECTED ME
Example	Mom was diagnosed with cancer.	I felt alone and afraid.
	Mom took me on a special trip.	I felt special and important.
	Mom had to go back to work.	I felt unstable; I never knew who would be there when I got home.
0–1		
1–2		
2–4		
4–6		
6–10		
10–14		
14–18		
18–22		
22–26		
26–30		
30–35		
35–40		
40–45		
45–50		
50+		

Now I want you to think about your relationship with your dad or other primary caretaker. First, fill out the circles on the worksheet and then identify significant memories or events using the chart below.

AGE	MEMORY	HOW IT AFFECTED ME
Example	Dad wasn't there to give me direction or guidance.	I felt alone and disoriented.
	Dad was always home for family dinner.	I felt seen and heard.
	Dad was harsh in his spankings or punishments.	I felt uptight and afraid. I never knew what would set him off.
0–1		
1–2		
2–4		
4–6		
6–10		
10–14		
14–18		
18–22		
22–26		
26–30		
30–35		
35–40		
40–45		
45–50		
50+		

For some of you that was no big deal, and for others of you, that was one of the hardest things you've ever done. If that is you, I am so sorry. If remembering is too difficult for you to do alone or causes you to go to some really dark places, I want you to stop and consider doing this exercise in the presence of a godly counselor you trust. It might take a long time to build that trust in a counseling relationship, and it might even take a while to find the right counselor, but don't stop or give up because it's too hard or demands too much in the way of time, emotional energy, or financial resources. If you quit, you will stay stuck. Buried memories will surface in destructive ways later. So please get the help you need to press through to freedom and restorative life that waits on the other side.

A great resource to find a Christian counselor in your area is the American Association of Christian Counselors at aacc.net.

For those of you who can press on now, keep your place here in the workbook but turn back to Day Three from last week, and look back at the four questions from Dr. Gregg Jantz.

- Am I worthy of being loved?
- Am I able to do what I need to do to get the love I need?
- Are other people reliable and trustworthy?
- Are other people accessible and willing to respond to me when I need them?[13]

What answers to those four questions did you identify with? Take a moment to write those answers one more time in the space provided on the worksheet.

Now look back at the memories you wrote down with your mom and your dad (or other primary caretakers) and the way those memories affected you. Circle any that line up with or are similar to the answers you just wrote.

Are you able to see a correlation between your attachment style with your parents, especially in those early, formative years, and the way you now answer those four basic questions? If so, what is the correlation? In other words, how is your ability to feel secure and loved in the here and now affected by your memories with your parents and the way those memories affected you?

Friends, you just did one of the hardest parts of the whole restoration process. You were honest about your past and the way it still affects your present. Now you are ready for the next hard part to begin: you learn how to invite Christ into those memories and give you a new lens through which to see your past and relate to others in your present.

Tomorrow we'll continue the hard work of remembering, but let's close today inviting God to come in and hold what we cannot hold ourselves as He leads us down a path that will restore our souls.

Respond

Father,
"Your word is a lamp to my feet and a light to my path" (Psalm 119:105). It is not a search beam that lights up the whole sky, but a lamp that shows me the next step. Help me to hold Your Word close to my heart, thoughts, and steps today, and show me where to take the next step. If pain or hard memories continue to surface, remind me You are with me in the valley, showing me where to take the next step towards healing.

Continuing the Calm

If you feel uncomfortable, anxious, or sad after walking down memory lane, give yourself a few minutes to bring calm back into your heart and mind. It may seem impossible to calm your mind when your thoughts are racing but controlling your body's reaction is like a backdoor into emotional stillness.

Begin by noticing what is happening in your body in reaction to the things you've been considering. Is your heart racing? Do you have pain in your stomach? Is there tightness in any of your muscles? Notice these and begin taking slow, deep breaths. As you do, focus on your breathing, and make sure you breathe out for longer than you breathe in. One way to try this is to breathe in your nose for a count of four, hold for four, and breathe out your mouth for a count of six. If you have numbers that you like better, use those.

Give yourself time with this. Focus on the ins and outs of your breathing. Notice any tension and tell your body to relax in these areas. In doing so, you are showing your brain that there is no current threat and it is safe to relax. If you have a favorite Bible verse that reminds you of God's nearness, begin to dwell on it as you breathe in and out.

After a few minutes of breathing, however long it takes, imagine bringing any remaining anxiety or sadness and placing it in the hands of your Savior. He is with you. You are safe to place all your fears in His hands and to allow Him to replace them with His peace.

DAY 4

Read

Today's Personal Study refers to book chapter 5, "How We Remember," and chapter 6, "Remembering in the Storms."

Reflect

Yesterday we started the hard work of remembering the events that led to our attachment style with our parents or primary caretakers. Today, I want to continue remembering and learning to see how our past affects our present-day behavior and relationships. The goal isn't to bring shame—it's to bring anything in the dark to the light so we can be restored, redeemed, and healed.

Look back at your memories with your parents or caretakers and the effects those memories had on you. I want you to continue to think through how that foundational relationship with your mom and dad and the ways you learned to relate to them affects the ways you relate to every other person in your life.

If you are married, I want you to think about your relationship with your spouse. If you are single, think about a significant romantic relationship that is either current or in the past. Think of three words to describe how you most often relate to your spouse or boyfriend or girlfriend, and then write those words in the circles on the worksheet.

Now look back at your attachment style and predominant memories with your parents or caretakers. What correlation, if any, do you see between the ways you most often relate to your spouse and your attachment style?

If you have children, think about your relationship with them. Think of three words to describe how you most often relate to your children, and then write those words in the circles on the worksheet.

Now review your answers to Dr. Jantz's four questions. How do you think your own children would answer those questions? Write what you think their answers would be in the space provided on the worksheet.

Is it similar to the way you answered those same questions? Explain.

One more round of questions—take a deep breath, and remember, with the help of the Word of God, the Spirit of God and the grace He gives, you can do this.

Think about three important friendships that have defined your life. They can be friends from childhood, adolescence, college, or adulthood. Write their names in the circle on the worksheet.

Think of three words would you use to most often describe the relationship between you and those friends and write them on the worksheet.

Now once again, look back at your attachment style and predominant memories with your parents or caretakers. What correlation, if any, exists between the ways you most often relate to friends and your attachment style?

If this is the first time you have done anything like this and you are anything like me, right about now you need to be scooped up off the floor. It is so hard to look at the pain and hurt in relationships that seem to draw a consistent pattern across the backdrop of our lives.

But think back to what we learned from chapter 1 in the book: how we attach to our parents determines with 80% accuracy how we will attach to every other person in our lives.[14] Patterns of pain and insecurity in relationship with our parents produce patterns of pain and insecurity in us that we pass on to our spouse, our children, and our friends. The dynamic of insecurity and hurt won't stop unless we look up and out to God for earned secure attachment and deliverance.

Now, think about your relationship with God. Remember, no one is seeing your answers here but you. Be as honest as you can. Think of three words you would you most often use to describe your relationship with Him and write them on the worksheet.

Now, you know the drill: think back to your attachment style and relationship with your parents. What correlation, if any, exists between how you attached to your parents and how you are now attached to and relate to God? Explain.

Most likely, most of us have a lot of work to do—work in our relationships with our parents, our spouse, our boyfriend or girlfriend, our children, and our friends. But here is our hope: the relationship we need to focus on first and foremost is our relationship with God. When we begin to securely attach to Him, no matter how unstable we feel anywhere and everywhere else, those other significant relationships in our life will begin to change as well.

Let's close today by reading Matthew 6:33 and then writing it out word-for-word at the top of your worksheet.

What are we to seek first? As we do, what then will be added to us? Explain in your own words.

The word "righteousness" simply means this: right relationship with God and with others. As you seek right relationship with God, right relationships will be added everywhere else. The way you learn to relate to Him as your good Father will affect how you relate to every other person in your life as well. That's just how it works.

That's where we'll start tomorrow—right relationship with God. So, for the rest of your day, go about with a peace-filled heart, knowing you've done the hardest part: you've cracked the lid of your past to see how it is affecting your present. And now that those things are out in the open, with God at the top as your priority above every relationship, you can start to restore.

Respond

Father,
You never said healing would be easy, but You've promised to be with me every step of the way. Shepherd my heart, guide my steps, and restore my relationship with You first and then with the people in my life with whom I need a fresh start and a fresh way of relating. Thank You that even when my circumstances or relationships with others feel unstable or unsteady, my heart can be at rest and secure in You.

DAY 5

Read

Today's Personal Study refers to the book's chapter 5, "How We Remember" and chapter 6, "Remembering in the Storms."

Reflect

Today I want us to take the broken pieces and attachment from our past and put them all under a new banner, a banner called *Earned Secure Attachment.*

Earned secure attachment is available to anyone and everyone who is willing to go on a journey of transferring their primary attachment and learned ways of relating and reacting in relationships from their earthly parents to God. Frankly, even if you grew up securely attached to your parents, this is a journey every believer in Christ must make. It is what grows us into mature adults who flourish in the kingdom of God.

We move toward earned secure attachment as we tell our story to an empathetic listener who then invites us to hear it through a different lens. (Spoiler alert: you'll read about this in chapter seven of the book.)

Earned secure attachment is that simple and that hard. Every day, we regularly and routinely sit down with the God who loves us and gave the life of His Son to redeem us, and we tell Him our stories—the good, the bad, and the ugly. And then we must sit still enough for long enough to hear Him tell our stories back to us through the true and transforming lens of His Word. Finally, we must do what His Word says. Simply put, we learn to trust and obey.

Are you ready to learn how to begin a lifelong process of moving towards earned secure attachment with God, your stable, secure, faithful, present, and perfect primary caretaker, that will then change and affect every other relationship in your life?

If you get stuck, here are some words to help you process your memory: angry, resentful, afraid, sad, tense, uneasy, dread, ashamed, worried, alone, panicked, lost, horrified, alarmed, anxious, disappointed. Choose one and use it to help you pray.

Step 1: Remember the Past

Look back at your chart of memories from your mom or your dad. Choose one hard memory that stands out. Consider how it made you feel and write the details of that memory and the emotions that still accompany it as a prayer or cry to the Lord in the space provided.

Here are some words to help you if you get stuck: alone, afraid, ashamed, victim, orphan, not enough, overlooked, replaceable, irredeemable, unwanted.

Step 2: Remember Your Identity

In that memory, what agreement did you make with the enemy of your soul about your identity? Who did you start believing you were? Confess this to the Lord.

Here are some possibilities:

- I can't trust anyone.
- I am on my own to take care of myself.
- I will keep up walls to make sure I will never be hurt that way again.
- Rejection or betrayal in relationships is inevitable.
- I will overperform and overgive in relationships to keep abandonment at bay.

Step 3: Remember Your Possibilities

In that memory, what agreement did you make with the enemy of your soul about the direction of your life and your possibilities in the present and future? Tell God about it.

Step 4: Restore Through God's Word

Now I want you to hear and see that same memory through the lens of God's Word. Turn to Isaiah 43:1–3.

Who does God say He is?

Who does God say you are?

When trials come and tough things happen, where does God say He is?

What are the possibilities for your life, even though hard things have happened?

What is God's command for you to trust and obey?

Step 5: Restore the Past

Take the truth of what you just read in Isaiah 43:1–3, and rewrite that same memory below. This time, apply the reality that God is who He says He is in His Word—He was with you in every moment of the storm. You can even close your eyes and ask God to show you where He was and what He was doing in that painful moment. Even if you can't "see" anything with your physical eyes, ask that God would "enlighten the eyes of your heart" to help you know the hope to which He has called you, the riches of what He has prepared for you, and the immeasurable greatness of His power toward you who believe the truth of His promises and His Word (Ephesians 1:18–19). Write it out as if you were sitting down with God, telling Him face to face about that moment.

Step 6: Restore Your Identity

Repeat back to God the truth about who He says you are from the passage in Isaiah. Consider starting with something like, "I know now that I am . . . "

Step 7: Restore Your Possibilities

According to the truth of Isaiah 43:1–3, what does God say about the direction of your life and the possibilities He has for you in the present and future? Express to Him your confidence that He is the one who directs your path and nothing and no one can stand in the way of His plan. Tell Him your life is defined by His redemptive presence, not your broken past.

Step 8: Rebuild

This is the last step. This is where we draw the line in the sand with the enemy of our souls and declare loud and clear that we are putting on a new lens through which we will see the story of our lives.

This step of rebuilding always happens through repentance, so write out a prayer repenting for ignoring God's Word and choosing to see your past, your identity, and your possibilities through the old lens for so long. Tell Him you are putting on your new lens of His presence with you, your identity of who He says you are, and the possibilities about your life and how He says you are to walk in it.

Can I do a huge jump for joy and tell you something? You just took your first step toward earned secure attachment. You just transferred your way of remembering and relating to your past to a new parent. This transfer won't hinder love for your earthly parents; it'll actually enable and you to experience and release it in a whole new way. Your love for them doesn't depend on their past performance. It depends on the love of a Father who has been with you and them every step of the way.

And now you know what to do for other memories that need to be healed. This exercise of remembering, restoring, and rebuilding is how you and I grow toward earned secure attachment. This is also why the journey of moving toward earned secure attachment takes longer than we usually think. After living for decades on planet earth, we have a lot of pain and hardship to process. But restoration is available if we will continue to bring every hard memory, every walled off place, and every buried hurt that surfaces, to the Father of our spirit who says, "You are mine. Do not fear. It's time to live."

To help you continue to process through hard things in the days ahead, go to **susannahbaker.com/freetools** to get free, printable worksheets with these same steps of prayer. The worksheets also include a list of verses to use to help you remember, restore, and rebuild from other painful memories in your past or present.

Respond

Father,

Thank You for the gift of earned secure attachment. As I do the hard work of learning how to remember my past through the faithful and true lens of Your Word, I know You will restore my soul and rebuild my past and present, preparing me for my future. Give me the courage to keep walking this journey of restoration one memory, one day, one step at a time, always remembering I am Yours and You are with me

WEEK 3

Let the Restoration Begin

Derek Kinder

If forgiveness is good, fellowship is better

Surround: encompass me about

* the blessed person is the honest person. What stays in the dark stays unrestored.

VIEWER GUIDE: WEEK 3

RESTORING THROUGH THE PSALMS

- Earned secure attachment occurs through telling your __________ to an empathetic __________ who invites you to see and imagine your story through a different __________.
  - Your story is the __________ of your __________.
  - Your primary listener is your __________ who is in __________.
  - Your primary means of telling your story are times of __________ in reading God's __________ and __________.
  - Your lens is the __________ of __________ received through __________ with Jesus Christ.

- Through the Psalms, and specifically Psalm 32, we see:
  - restoration through __________ (v. 1)
  - restoration through __________ and __________ (vv. 2–5)
  - restoration through __________ (vv. 6–7)
  - restoration through __________ (vv. 8–9)
  - restoration through __________ and steadfast __________ (vv. 10–11)

Video Sessions available at susannahbaker.com/biblestudies.

PERSONAL STUDY

Before beginning this week's study, please read chapters 7–9 of the book.

DAY 1

Read

Today's Personal Study refers to chapter 7 in the book, "Restoring Through Earned Secure Attachment."

Reflect

Last week you did some very hard, but good work. You began to pry the lid from your past and take an honest look at your attachment style to your parents and how that attachment style has affected every other relationship in your life.

But you also took some very important steps toward healing. Yes, you looked at your past honestly, but you also began to look at your God honestly—who He tells us He is and what He can do in His Word—and the lens on your life began to change. You started the process of trading your old lens of abandonment, betrayal, fear, depression, and isolation for the new lens of God's steadfast love and faithfulness.

As we start our work this week of digging into the restoration process, I want you to pause and think about your lens for life.

If you could sum up in one word the lens from the past through which you most often saw your life, what would it be?

Now what is the new lens through which you want to learn to see your life?

So how do you get there? How do you change your primary lens from being rejected to beloved, afraid to courageous, isolated and independent to trusting and dependent? We have to be courageous and persistent enough to do the hard work of *earned secure attachment.*

Last week, I gave you a spoiler alert by giving you the definition of earned secure attachment. Look at page 86 in your book, and write the definition in the space provided.

Earned Secure Attachment:

Earned secure attachment is so simple, yet oh so hard. It doesn't require a master's degree or doctorate, but what it does require is a willingness to show up and be honest about yourself, your sin, your shortcomings, your failures, and the messes in your life on a day in and day out basis.

But here is the exciting and encouraging part: as I began to learn about my own broken, insecure attachment and the hope found in moving toward earned secure attachment, I realized God had given me, along with every other believer, three primary tools to use in making that journey.

Look at page 87 in your book and write what those tools are.

Like I said last week, for a Christian, moving to a place of earned secure attachment is impossible without learning to meditate on and pray the Word of God. God is not just our Friend, Judge, Savior, Redeemer, or Lord—He is our Father, our primary caretaker. To transfer our broken, insecure attachment from our earthly parents to God Himself requires knowing who He is and exactly what He promises to do in our lives. And we discover and learn those things in His Word. Then, we take what we learn about God in His Word, and we sow it as seeds in the present through trust and prayer. Again, it's that simple and that hard.

We can go to church, listen to sermons, attend small groups, and even memorize verses or study Scripture, but if we fail to do the work of meditating and praying, we will stay stuck in our insecure attachment. It doesn't mean you are not a believer, but it does mean you are missing out on all that is offered to you as a securely beloved child.

You and I have all met people who attended church and listened to hundreds of sermons but remain unchanged. But personally speaking, I have never met a man or woman who spends ample time on their knees claiming, asking, believing, and trusting in the person and character of God who isn't different. Changed. At peace. Perhaps lowly in the eyes of the world but powerful and mighty in the spirit.

That's who I want to be and where I want to go—I want to continue taking the journey of becoming a securely attached child of God who knows and is known by her heavenly Father.

But what does meditating on God's Word and prayer really look like? That is what we will discover throughout the rest of the week. For now, I want to close today by reading one of my favorite passages in all of Scripture, Psalm 1:1–6. This psalm is the lens, or gateway psalm, by which we see every other psalm that comes after it.

Read Psalm 1:1–6.

What three things does a "blessed" person not do (v. 1)?

What does the blessed person delight in, and how do they show their delight (v. 2)?

What does this person become (v. 3)?

The blessed person is the one who "meditates" on God's Word, which simply means "to think out its implications for all life."[15] But this meditation isn't a forced exercise; it's done out of delight, a delight that flows naturally from a person who lingers long in God's Word and loves what they discover. The implication is that the blessed person is the one who actually loves what God commands.

She loves that instead of brokenness and bitterness, God's way offers restoration and peace. She loves that instead of worry and fear, God's way offers trust, dependency, and peace. Quite simply, she loves the person of God behind every command.

As you and I walk this road of earned secure attachment, we will become like those trees whose leaves are evergreen, drinking from a source of water that never fails. While our circumstances may not change, the place we go and the parent to whom we turn is none other than God Himself. And as we walk with our wise God in the counsel of His good Word instead of the doubt, pride, despair and weariness of our own hearts, the lens on our life begins to change.

Respond

Father,

The lens on my life of _________ (put the name of your old lens here) has been in place for far too long. I am ready to make a change, Lord. I am ready to open myself up and allow You to restore my soul. As I read Your Word, think through its implications for my life, and pray its promises back to You, please change my lens of life to be _________ (put the name of your new lens here). Thank You that You stand ready and waiting to be known as my trusted heavenly Father and for me to know You as Your securely beloved child.

DAY 2

Read

Today's Personal Study refers to chapter 7, "Restoring Through Earned Secure Attachment."

Reflect

Yesterday we started to unpack the definition of earned secure attachment and look at the tools we need to restore and move from insecure to secure attachment. Our tools help us to tell our story to two primary and needed audiences:

1. To God
2. To others

We cannot become securely attached to God unless we use the tool of God's Word. We must learn to meditate on it, allowing it to transform the lens through which we see life, and we must learn to pray it back to Him, trusting and believing its promises.

Today, I want to spend time talking about the second tool we have at our disposal—the Psalms.

The Psalms are considered "the medicine cabinet" or the healing ointment for broken hearts and shattered lives, right in the middle of our Bibles. They are powerful because they are accounts of people's stories—their raw, honest, assessments of how they processed the hurts, disappointments, betrayals, fears, and general disappointments in life, while learning to see everything through a lens of gratitude, acceptance, and praise. They are our invitation to insert our own stories and broken experiences into the Psalms as well and watch what God can do with a broken story and a shattered heart.

Meditating and praying through all of Scripture is good, but while working specifically on moving toward a place of earned secure attachment, I found the Psalms a particularly helpful place to help me learn how to process my emotions rightly before the face of God and to learn to see life through a whole new lens.

Before I even knew the term "earned secure attachment" existed, I had been reading and praying through the Psalms for several years. Every morning, I would begin my day by reading through a psalm, reading a commentary on the Psalms (Tim Keller's *The Songs of Jesus* and Derek Kidner's two volume commentary on the Psalms are two of my favorites), and then stopping to meditate on and pray through one or two verses that really grabbed my attention.

I would set my timer for five minutes and pour out my heart to God in my journal, telling Him my struggles with my very real self and very real other people. Then I would take the truth found in the psalm and apply it to my situation. I would repent for any attitudes of doubt, unbelief, fear, hatred, envy, or heaviness the Psalm highlighted and then ask God to help me receive the response of trust, belief, forgiveness, contentment, or gratitude it modeled.

Through the Psalms, I discovered no emotion was off limits, and no mess or failure of mine was too much for God to address, clean up, or forgive. Every morning I met with my God who—to my surprise—got down on His hands and knees to clean me up, tend to my wounds, comfort my heart, and give me a new lens through which to see the specifics of my day, situation, and life. The Psalms became God's standing invitation for me to tell Him my story and to hear it repeated through a different lens.

Like the way I processed the lens of my past from long-ago memories, I processed the emotions of pain that surfaced in my heart on a regular basis. Over a period of several years—as I prayed through my reactive and sometimes explosive patterns and habits of relating to people around me from my insecure-ambivalent style of attachment—the lies I believed and the truth from God's Word that I needed to replace those lies with built in me earned secure attachment.

If you have an insecure-avoidant style of attachment, your patterns of relating to people around you might involve more withdrawing or punishing in angry silence than reacting. But for either attachment style, this way of praying through remembering, restoring, and rebuilding can be incredibly healing as you learn to process your story before the God who listens and responds through His Spirit and His Word.

Today, I want to walk you through that process using Psalm 46 so you can follow the template and use it for your time of meditation and prayer every day, not just for the hard things that have happened in the past, but for the insecure patterns of relating to others on a day-to-day basis where you feel stuck.

If you get stuck, here are some words to help you get started: frustrated, irritated, exhausted, weary, stuck, confused, numb, joyless, worried.

Step 1: Remember the Past

Set a timer for five minutes and use the space provided to tell God exactly where you are today. Remember, no emotion is off limits or mess too big to clean up.

Step 2: Remember Your Identity

What agreement are you making with the enemy of your soul today about your identity? Tell God what you believe about His availability to you based on your performance or circumstances.

Step 3: Remember Your Possibilities

What agreement are you making with the enemy of your soul today about the direction of your life and your possibilities in the present and future? Write out what you believe about your ability to change.

Step 4: Restore Through God's Word

Now I want you to hear, see, and process your life through the lens of God's Word. Read Psalm 46:1–11.

Who does God say He is (v. 1)?

When does God say He is a refuge, strength, and present help (vv. 1–2)?

What should our response be to who God is, no matter the state of our circumstances?

When trials come and tough things happen, where does God say that He is (vv. 4–7)?

What are the possibilities for your life, even though hard things have happened (vv. 10–11)?

What are God's commands for you to trust and obey in these verses?

Step 5: Restore the Past

Take the truth of what you just read in Psalm 46:1–11, and rewrite your same circumstances below, but this time, apply the reality that God is who He says He is in that passage—He is your refuge, strength, and very present help in time of trouble . . . even trouble of your own making. Even if you can't "see" anything with your physical eyes, ask that God would "enlighten the eyes of your heart" to help you be still enough to know the hope to which He has called you, the riches of what He has prepared for you, and the immeasurable greatness of His power toward you who believe the truth of His promises and His Word (Ephesians 1:18–19). Write it out as if you were sitting down with God, telling Him face to face about that circumstance.

Step 6: Restore Your Identity

According to the truth of Psalm 46:1–11, who does God say you are, despite the things that have happened? Consider starting with something like, "I know now that I am . . . despite what I've done (be specific) or when I've experienced difficult things because of others' actions (again, be specific here).

Step 7: Restore Your Possibilities

According to the truth of Psalm 46:1–11, what does God say about the direction of your life and the possibilities He has for you in the present and future? Express to God your confidence that He is your Source for every good thing, no matter your circumstances. Tell Him that you trust Him to secure your heart and your future, no matter how unstable or insecure you feel.

Step 8: Rebuild

This is the last step. This is where we draw the line in the sand with the enemy of our souls and declare loud and clear that we are putting on a new lens through which we will see the story of our lives.

This rebuilding always happens through repentance, so in the space below, write out a prayer repenting for ignoring God's Word and choosing to see your past, your identity, and your possibilities through the old lens. Tell Him you are putting on your new lens of His presence with you, your identity of who He says you are, and your possibilities about your life and how He says you are to walk in it.

Friends, every day, you and I have a choice. We can process our lives and the very real brokenness that exists like we always have, through the same old lens, and stay stuck, or we can choose to put on the new lens of earned secure attachment through meditation on God's Word and prayer.

We do not tell our stories in a vacuum; we tell them to a God who listens and provides His Word as His response and as a lens through which to see all of life, the brokenness of others, and the messes of our own making.

To help you continue to process through hard things or everyday emotions in the days ahead, go to **susannahbaker.com/freetools** to get free, printable worksheets with these same steps of prayer.

I have also provided a list of psalms in the back of this workbook you can use daily to process through the very real emotions and insecure patterns and habits of your heart when it comes to restoring from insecure attachment. These are psalms that have been transformational for me in my own journey of healing.

I am so incredibly grateful that we serve a God who isn't afraid of our stories or worn out by our emotions. He is a God who loves to restore our souls and help us rebuild.

Respond

Father,

Every time I call on You, You answer me. You don't always remove my difficult circumstances, but You come to comfort me in my difficult circumstances. There isn't a mess I can make or a storm I can be caught in that You cannot clean up or calm. May the reality of Your presence with me in my past, present, and future help me be still, change the lens through which I see life, and know You are God.

DAY 3

Read

Today's Personal Study refers to chapter 7 in the book, "Restoring Through Earned Secure Attachment."

Reflect

This week, we have looked at the first two tools God has given us to work toward earned secure attachment—consistent time meditating on His Word through prayer and the book of Psalms. But before we take a moment to think through the third tool, I want to talk about the time it takes to implement the first two tools.

Remember, earned secure attachment is impossible without thoughtful, prayerful time in God's Word. So, when will you make time to regularly be in God's Word and prayer? What will this look like on a consistent daily basis for you?

Practically speaking, is there anything in your schedule that needs to be adjusted so that you can have this time? Do you need to be in bed by a certain time so you can wake up earlier? Do you need to adjust your exercise routine, carpool routine, or work routine to enable you to make this time to move toward your heavenly Father and securely attach?

Now that you have thought through how you will actively implement the first two tools, what is the third tool you have at your disposal to help you move toward earned secure attachment?

Realistically, I know not everyone will be able to see a counselor on a regular basis. You might have obstacles of finances, time, or counselor availability standing in your way. But hear me on this—if you can't tell your story with regularity to a counselor, you need to tell it to someone. And that someone needs to be someone safe who listens empathetically to your story and loves Jesus and will point you to Him.

Telling your story can occur at unplanned, random moments, like over a cup of coffee with a friend or standing in the driveway with a neighbor. But to see progress in your journey toward earned secure attachment, research shows that you need to tell your story to someone consistently for a year.

So here is the question: Who will you tell your story? A mentor? A trusted friend? A counselor? Name three to five different people. (You only need to meet consistently with one person but thinking of three to five names gives you options to work with.)

Now when will make the time to see this counselor, mentor, or friend? You need space in your week of at least an hour, maybe more if you consider travel time getting to or from your meeting or appointment. Think through your week and list two or three different time options.

How long will you commit to see this counselor, mentor, or friend? Once a week for a year, six months, or a month? Once a month for a year? Explain.

What in your schedule will need to go so you can create the time you need to restore and heal? Just like healing in our bodies takes effort and time, so does healing in our souls. Take a moment to think through your commitments each week and prayerfully consider what might need to be put on hold, paused, or stopped while you take this important step in restoration.

I had quiet times, prayer times, and time in God's Word for years. But it wasn't until I got serious about having regularly scheduled time in prayer to really process through God's Word and regularly scheduled time with a counselor that I saw breakthrough in my ability to trust God and move toward earned secure attachment.

I want to encourage you in one more thing: don't be discouraged if it takes you some time to connect with the right counselor, friend, or mentor. That's why I had you write down three to five names instead of just one.

When my husband, Jason, started his journey of healing and moving toward earned secure attachment, it took him two years to find the right counselor. During those two years, he met with three to four different counselors before finding the one he felt like he connected with on a deeply personal level. I don't say this to discourage but to encourage you—those two years were not wasted. In fact, they were an important part of his healing process. Healing was always a side-line item for Jason, something that took the backseat to work, family, or other priorities. He always felt like he just needed to be strong enough to muscle his way through the hurt, get over it, and move on.

But he finally got to a place where he couldn't pick himself up anymore. Healing wasn't a side-line item anymore—it became a necessity. During those two years, he struggled with depression in a way he had never struggled before. But God used his search for connection with an empathetic listener to tell his story to help him develop courage, strength, and perseverance in his soul. God also used that time to draw the two of us closer in our marriage. I learned to pray for and listen to Jason like I never had before. And then when the time was right and the right counselor came, Jason's growth was astronomical—almost overnight. Those two really hard, dark years were years of quiet, silent growth where Jason was learning to trust the Lord and His Word in a way he had never had to before. Those two hard years prepared the way for a third year of rapid healing and growth.

Read Hebrews 10:32–39.

When did the original recipients of this message endure "a hard struggle with sufferings"?

What did some of their sufferings include?

What did God's people need and why (v. 36)?

What kind of people is God building us into through our sufferings?

In no way do I mean to compare the sufferings of the persecuted church either in antiquity or today with the sufferings most of us endure. But what I am saying is this: the roadblocks, obstacles, and "hard struggle with sufferings" in our lives are given as a gift to build into us the endurance we need to live a life of faith and receive what is one day promised to us. Life with Christ isn't for the faint of heart; it's for the faith-filled, strong, persevering heart who is committed to following Christ, knowing Him, and being known—no matter how long or hard the road.

God knows exactly what you and I need in the journey ahead toward restoration. What Jason and I have both learned the past few years is that while everyone's tools are similar, no one's process is the same. But God knows exactly what process each person needs to heal their heart and move toward earned secure attachment. So, no matter what lies ahead for you, you can trust the process of your good God.

Respond

Father,
Your ways are so different than ours, and no one's process is ever the same. You use the tools of Your Word, prayer, and our telling our stories to one another in the body of Christ to move us to a place of security and trust with You as our good Father. Any and all suffering in our lives, You use to build steadfastness and godly character into us so that we will receive a rich welcome into our heavenly home one day (2 Peter 1:10–11). Help us seriously consider the time we need to take and obstacles we need to overcome to keep walking the path of healing and restoration with You.

DAY 4

Read

Today's Personal Study refers to chapter 8 in the book, "Restoring Through a Scaffolding."

Reflect

In her book *The Writing Life*, Annie Dillard points out, "How we spend our days is, of course, how we spend our lives. What we do with this hour, and that one, is what we are doing. A schedule defends from chaos and whim. It is a net for catching days. It is a scaffolding on which a worker can stand and labor with both hands at sections of time."[16]

The very nature of broken, insecure attachment makes you feel as if you are either floundering or paralyzed, in a perpetual state of fight or flight. During my darkest days with depression and anxiety, an established, secure schedule kept me grounded and enabled me to put one foot in front of the other when I didn't know what else to do.

For our purposes, I have chosen to represent a scaffolding through an image of a ladder with four different rungs. I want you to think through these four rungs carefully. What makes you, you? For you to labor all the days God has given you from a safe and secure place, what rungs do you need to stand on consistently?

For believers in Christ, one of the rungs on your ladder must be meditation on God's Word and prayer. Another rung for you in this season of life might be consistent counseling sessions or talking to someone you trust. Your other rungs could be painting, writing, cooking, running, coaching, teaching, or gardening. The list is as varied as the many ways God has made us. But there are things you need to be doing to flourish, grow, heal, restore, and have the time and space to move toward a place of earned secure attachment.

THE RUNGS TO RESTORE

Think through what those foundational things you need to do in order to restore, and write them directly on the rungs of the ladder. Remember—only one thing should go on each rung.

Now think through when you will create the time to insert those rungs regularly into your schedule each day or week and write that specific time beside each rung.

Read Luke 22:39–46.

Underline the phrase, "as was his custom" (v. 39).

Circle the phrase, "the place" (v. 40).

Put a box around what Jesus knelt and did in this place (v. 41).

How did God the Father respond to Jesus's request (v. 43)? Was this different from what you expected? Why or why not?

The night before Jesus died, we are given a sacred, intimate glimpse into how He processed the suffering ahead. He didn't do something new or extraordinary; He didn't give a news blast about what He was about to do to the city of Jerusalem or surrounding countryside. He did what He always did and what "his custom" was to do—He prayed.

In the Greek, the phrase "as was his custom" means "a usage (prescribed by habit or law)."[17] Jesus did not have to think about where to go or what to do when His life took a turn for the hard and horrible. He went to a familiar place—a place He was known to go—He knelt, and He prayed.

In fact, prayer in "the place," the Mount of Olives, was such a regular habit in Jesus's life, His disciple Judas knew right where to take the soldiers to find and arrest Him (Luke 22:47).

But here's the thing: the regular rungs on Jesus's ladder—time in God's Word and time in prayer processing all of life before the face of His Father—sustained Him in His time of greatest need. Because He didn't panic, or freak out, or become paralyzed, or go into flight or fight mode, He was able to process His greatest trial through prayer. He was able to find secure ground when everything around Him was shaking. And because of that, because of His practice of prayer, He was able to stand strong and drink the cup God had for Him to drink, the cup that saved you and me.

You and I will never be asked to drink the cup of God's wrath that Jesus drank on our behalf—but we will be asked to walk through suffering and trials. And just like Jesus, what we do with our ordinary moments, on our ordinary ladders, and on our ordinary days will direct the trajectory of our extraordinary moments. In moments of crisis and panic, we will know where to turn and how to kneel.

The salvation of humanity won't be at stake because of our habit of prayer and time in God's Word, but perhaps the saving of our children, our marriage, a friendship, or an unreached people group in Africa or India or China will be affected by it. Jesus is the only One who saves the souls of people, but He partners with us through our prayers to shape events that shape the souls of the people we love (see Genesis 18:22–33).

Our habit of prayer matters. Our rungs matter. The time we spend using the tools God has given to develop earned secure attachment in us matters. It's never too late to start standing on the rung of God's Word and prayer. Begin wherever you are—no matter the stage of life you are in—and let the healing and transformation begin. Not just for you, but for the people in your life, your sphere of influence, and your world that God has ordained for your prayers to shape.

Respond

Father,

It's so easy to waste my days. It's easy to look up and see a whole day, week, month, or year has passed, and I have remained the same. Please draw my heart through repentance, conviction, and the knowledge of Your Word to desiring to spend my time wisely. Show me how You want me to spend my day and the rungs of my ladder on which You want me to stand. Help me use my everyday moments well to move me toward a place of healing, restoration, and earned secure attachment to prepare me for any extraordinary moments up ahead.

DAY 5

Read

Today's Personal Study refers to chapter 9, "Restoring Through Persistent Prayer."

Reflect

The very first rung on our ladder and tool in our toolbox to help us restore and move toward earned secure attachment is so important. Let's take time to revisit it today.

We know that time spent in God's Word and prayer is important, but why is it so important? What's the big deal about having a persistent personal prayer life?

We may profess to believe God is good, all powerful, all capable, and can do what He says He will do. We may profess that we need Him to live our lives in wisdom, security, fruitfulness, and peace. And yet, our prayerlessness betrays us. Our prayer life, the time we spend in secret with the Father while no one else is looking, shows us our real beliefs about God. If we do not pray consistently, persistently, or scripturally, then what we really believe about God is that we can do life fine on our own. What we really believe about God is that He is not powerful enough or interested enough in us to answer us when we cry out. So, we don't pray. We learn to fend for ourselves and take care of our own needs, all the while we're withering inside and making a general mess of things.

Slowly read through the list of words below and circle the ones that resonate with you about your own personal prayer life. What do you really believe about prayer? Prayer is . . .

Boring	Intimate	Dependent
Dull	Vague	Vulnerable
Unnecessary	Specific	Difficult
Mysterious	Hopeful	Formal
Simple	Comforting	Real
Complicated	Rote	Hard
Childlike	Life-Giving	Easy
Personal	Life-Changing	Responsive
Only for Mature Christians	Pointless	Exhausting
Powerful	Necessary	

Read Matthew 6:5–15.

Look at verses 5–6, and then look at the words describing prayer above. Which words resonate with the way Jesus described prayer?

Let's pause and take the mystery out of prayer for a moment. Real prayer to a very real God is simply this: telling your story to an empathetic listener who then invites you to hear it through a different lens.

Does this definition sound familiar? It should. It's the same definition for earned secure attachment. The best way you and I can build new neural pathways in our brains, restore, heal, and learn to see life through a different lens day in and day out is . . . pray. Prayer isn't supposed to be complicated or mysterious. It's supposed to be a very real way for a very real Father to connect with the very real needs and hearts of His children. Through prayer, we tell God our "story," the very real details of our very real day.

Reread verse 11. What kind of things did Jesus say we should be asking God for on a regular basis?

We cannot ask God for daily needs unless we are telling Him our daily story—the big things and small things that happen to us throughout our day. Yes, we are to ask God about things in war torn countries, impoverished people groups, and the persecuted church. But we are also supposed to ask Him about the daily needs and condition of our very own hearts.

If our story is the details of our life—past, present, and future—who is our empathetic listener (see v. 6)?

How many times in these verses did Jesus use the title "Father" for God when talking about prayer? Circle or underline every occurrence in your Bible.

What does this tell us about the nature of prayer? What should our posture be when we go to God in prayer?

Read Matthew 4:4. What did Jesus say is the "different lens" we are invited to see our lives and hear our stories through?

Now that we know what we are praying about and who we are praying to, let's take a moment to look at how we pray.

Read Luke 11:1–8.

What request did Jesus's disciple make of Him (v. 1)?

Jesus told His disciples a parable or story to illustrate how we should pray (vv. 5–8). Fill in the blank from verse 8.

"I tell you, though he will not get up and give him anything because he is his friend, yet because of his ______________ he will rise and give him whatever he needs."

Different translations of Scripture use different words or phrases for this word, but my favorites are "shameless boldness" (CSB) and "persistence" (NKJV).

I don't know about you, but out of all the attributes Jesus could have highlighted or emphasized about a prayerful person, impudent, shamelessly bold, persistent aren't words I would have picked first. Holy? Yes. Quiet? Yes. Reserved, appropriate, polite, or respectful? Absolutely. But to tell His disciples to ask with shameless, impudent, bold persistence pushes the limits on my definition of prayer. It sounds like He is telling us to ask like a child.

Think about it for a moment: who are the boldest, most audacious, persistent, shameless askers on the planet? Children. Children ask their parents for inappropriate requests (like new toys) at inappropriate times (like the day after Christmas). Or they ask for snacks (in a loud voice) when you are on the phone with their teacher for a conference. Or for you to bring them water, scratch their backs, or clean up their throw up in the middle of the night when the rest of the world is asleep.

Securely attached children ask the way they do when they believe they have a good parent who has the power and supply to give them what they want or need. The danger isn't a child who asks; the danger is a child who doesn't ask and remains quiet.

So you pray and you ask. Persistently. Shamelessly. Boldly. Over and over and over again. But does God always give us what we want?

Read Luke 11:9–13.

Does God always answer when we knock on the door in prayer (vv. 9–10)?

What does God promise to give us when we knock on the door in prayer (v. 13)?

God does not promise to always give us good circumstances, but He does promise the power and presence of a good Father in those circumstances. Prayer characterized by persistence keeps us dependent on God's promises, provision, and presence on a day-by-day, situation-by-situation, moment-by-moment basis.

God doesn't give us enough bread for the next ten years or even ten days—He gives us daily bread, enough for the next step. Quite frankly, that's all our small hearts can handle. We are not wise enough or strong enough to carry a heavy load of provisions that lasts for years, months, or even days at a time. All we can handle is the load for a day. God carries the load for our lives, and eternity, on His shoulders. Our job is to continually trust Him and go to Him daily for bread.

Review the words you chose to describe your prayer life and read over the list again. How has your perspective changed? What one or two words would you like to use to describe your personal prayer life? Explain.

Now close by asking your Father to turn your dull, boring, disinterested view of prayer into one that is personal, persistent, bold, childlike, and dependent. And then stand back and watch with expectation as He answers. Let the healing begin.

Respond

Father,
Thank You for carrying the heavy load of my life and the lives of the people I love; I trust You to give me what I need for each day as I depend on You through prayer and the daily bread of Your Word. Please help me to make prayer a priority, and teach me how to tell You, my good Father, my story. Help me learn to hear the story of my life through the life-changing lens of Your Word.

WEEK 4

Persistent Prayer

VIEWER GUIDE: WEEK 4

RESTORING THROUGH PRAYER

WHY PRAYER IS RESTORATIVE
MATTHEW 6:5–15

- We pray to our ____________________
  - Prayer is the language of ____________________.
  - As the church, we have much to learn from adoptive parents and adopted kids about our ____________________ in prayer. From them we can learn how we move in our __________________ from orphan to adopted, unwanted to beloved, and overlooked and unnoticed to chosen and wanted.

HOW PRAYER IS RESTORATIVE

- Consistent prayer keeps us ______________, ______________, and ______________ ______________ to God as His children.
- As a child, you needed the following six things from your parents:
  - ___________________________ (Psalm 139:1–6, 13–16)
  - ___________________________ (Psalm 139:7–12, 17–18)

- ____________________________ (Psalm 139:1–6)
- ability to ____________________________ your arousal (Psalm 139:7–12, 19–24)
- strong enough to handle your ____________________________ emotions (Psalm 139:7–12, 19–22)
- willingness to ____________________________[18] (Psalm 139:23–24)

- As we pray, regularly telling our story to God, who invites us to hear it through a different lens, we shift our primary attachment from our ______________ parents to our ______________ Father, looking to ______________ to meet our six attachment needs.

Video Sessions available at susannahbaker.com/biblestudies.

PERSONAL STUDY

Before beginning this week's study, please refer to chapter 9 and read chapters 10–12 of the book.

DAY 1

Read

Today's Personal Study refers to chapter 9 of the book, "Restoring Through Persistent Prayer."

Reflect

Like we talked about last week, making time to be in God's Word and to pray is an essential part of our journey toward restoration and healing. Look back at Day 5 of the Personal Study from last week to answer these next few questions.

What is our working definition for both earned secure attachment and prayer?

When it comes to prayer, what are our "stories"?

Who is our "listener"?

What is our "lens"?

We cannot know God, grow in prayer, and put on a different lens through which we see our lives unless we use the tool of God's Word. We must learn to read, study, and think long and hard about it, allowing it to transform the lens through which we see life. And then we must learn to pray God's Word back to Him, trusting and believing its promises.

But learning to pray persistently and securely is so hard. It requires endurance, strength, and determination—especially when you have to get up in the early morning hours or stay up after everyone else is asleep to have a consistent prayer life.

Life moves so fast and my brain has to work so hard every day to come up with basic things like a carpool schedule for four kids and what everyone will eat for dinner, that when I slow down enough for prayer, I need to have a plan in place for what I am going to pray about, or prayer doesn't happen. I am simply too overwhelmed to know where to begin or too tired to come up with the words.

I found that when I had specific prompts in front of me and a set time of prayer, then thought through what I wanted to ask God ahead of time, it was much easier to make prayer a daily habit instead of an emergency-only habit. Jesus Himself sets this example for us in the Gospels and often went away for extended times of solitude and prayer to be alone with His heavenly Father.

When can you set aside time each day for prayer? How much time can you allow yourself?

Where will you go to pray (your favorite cozy chair, the kitchen table, the front porch)?

Once you've settled where and when you'll pray, you can focus on the prompts. Several years before I learned the phrase "earned secure attachment"—or that such an idea even existed—I came up with a simple format for how to pray using the acronym PRAY: Praise, Repent, Ask, and Yield. This habit of persistent prayer held my heart through many dark days and prepared the way for a more restorative way of praying. Now that I have been through several years of processing patterns of behavior through what I like to call restorative prayer—repenting, restoring, and rebuilding—I find myself going back to this basic, persistent way of praying. I use restorative prayer as specific incidents occur instead of daily. Maybe this is where you are too.

I am only going to give a brief overview of each section of prayer in our personal study today, but if you would like to know more about this topic of persistent prayer, you can find my teaching series and a guided step-by-step process for praising, repenting, asking, and yielding in my prayer guide, *Secure: Connecting to God Through Persistent Prayer* at **susannahbaker.com/prayer-guides.**

If restorative, soul-searching, truth-telling prayer just seems too daunting or hard at first then start here with simple persistent prayer. The point is to position yourself before a Father who is listening, waiting, and ready to respond. As you begin to persistently pray, like me, you will begin to trust that He is a God who answers. He may not always answer how we want Him to, but He always gives us His good presence. Little by little, we build a relationship and language of trust with Him, and our hearts begin to open more and more. Then we naturally start showing up with the hard stuff, the big stuff, and the deep and heavy stuff instead of a wish list of petitions.

The goal in and through every season of life—no matter where you are on your journey of trust or prayer—is simply this: pray. Then step back and watch what God will do. Wherever you are, I want to walk you through the process of learning to tell your story to God consistently and persistently.

The prompts here are like the ones I use in restorative prayer and *Remember the Past*. I have found there are specific seasons in my life for each one.

Sometimes I need to pray in a restorative fashion simply for myself and the issues concerning my heart, and other times I just need to pray. To rouse myself and get into the habit of prayer for specific things in my life, for the people I love, and for God's kingdom to go out in power and love to the dark, hurting world around me.

Now let's begin to P-R-A-Y through lens of God's Word, using Matthew 6:9–13 as our guide.

Praise

Our Father in heaven,
your name be honored as holy.
—Matthew 6:9 CSB

As you've remembered your past rightly over the last few weeks, list a few things from your past that you can praise God for. (Think about how you've seen His character on display in your life. How has He loved, protected, been merciful to, and provided for you? You can look back at Week 1, Day 5 if you need help.)

Now, write it out. Use the list you made to praise and thank God for who He is and who He is to you. Thank Him for being trustworthy.

Repent

And forgive us our debts,
as we also have forgiven our debtors.
—Matthew 6:12 CSB

Restoring our souls always involves repentance, so write out a prayer repenting to God for ignoring His Word and choosing to see your day, your identity, your possibilities, your relationships, and the world around you through any lens that stands in contradiction to His Word.

Now tell Him you are putting on the new lens of His presence with you, the identity of who He says you are, and the possibilities about your life and how He says you are to walk in it.

Ask

Give us today our daily bread.
—Matthew 6:11 CSB

God loves to fulfill the promises He makes in His Word—but He loves for us to ask (Luke 11:9–10). Here is where you take the truth of God's Word and use it to help you ask scripturally and consistently for what you need each day. It's okay to ask God for what you need, and for that matter, what others need too.

Sometimes it helps me to think through the needs of the people or things I am asking for most consistently and make a schedule of what day of the week I will pray about specific things. The more specific I am, the greater the likelihood I will actually pray. The more general and vaguer I am, the more overwhelmed I become and the less I pray.

For more help in thinking through this area of asking, see the ask section in my prayer guide, *Secure: Connecting to God Through Persistent Prayer*.

Think through what God has put on your heart to pray, and then be persistent about praying for those things. Write out this part of your prayer below.

Yield

Your kingdom come.
Your will be done
on earth as it is in heaven.
—Matthew 6:10

Here is where we allow God to examine our hearts and show us if there is a command for our life or for our day we need to yield to, trust, or obey (see Psalm 139:23–24). Here is where we also release our circumstances, worries, and needs into our Father's hands and yield to the goodness and mercy He promises to give (see Psalm 23:6). Take time to write out a prayer of yielding in the space below.

Remember, the goal is not to pray perfectly; it's to pray persistently. It's to show up, and keep showing up, knocking on the door, believing you have a good Father on the other side ready and waiting to open and give you what you need for every day—His good presence (Luke 11:9–12). As you show up, what you will find is that through prayer and through God's Word, your soul will be restored one step, one day at a time.

Respond

Father,

Learning to pray persistently is a lifelong task. But I ask for the willingness to begin the process, wherever I am in my walk with You. Help me overcome my fear of thinking I need to say big words or be deeply knowledgeable about the Bible to pray. All that is required is a willingness to trust and depend on You. Keep me connected to Your Word so I know what to pray and how to ask and keep me securely attached to You as my good Father through the practice of persistent prayer all my days.

DAY 2

Read

Today's Personal Study refers to chapter 10 of the book, "Restoring Through Lament."

Reflect

As we learn to pray persistently before God while moving toward earned secure attachment, there are two tools to help us immensely. Those are the tools of lament and praise. Today and tomorrow, I want to dive in on what it looks like to lament in our prayers, and the last two days of this week, I want to learn how to use the tool of praise.

Before I began to move toward a place of earned secure attachment with the Lord through prayer, I used to think I had to start every prayer with praise or thanksgiving: "Lord, I thank You for this day. Or I praise You for Your goodness in this hard circumstance. Or I am so thankful for Your love, even though it's not anything I am feeling or seeing in my day-to-day life right now."

But as I started to study and pray the Psalms, my posture in prayer suddenly began to change. Like so many of the psalmists, I realized I didn't have to start with a song on my lips or thanksgiving in my heart. I could start with anger toward an enemy or friend. Frustration with my husband or children. Sorrow about a loss, transition, or season of change. Exhaustion and weariness from my daily responsibilities as a wife, mom, daughter, sister, neighbor, author, Bible study teacher, and friend. In a word, I could start with lament.

This one shift in perspective changed everything for me. It wasn't that praise or thanksgiving weren't important parts of prayer—it was just that I didn't have to *start* there. The Psalms showed me I could start with honesty, openness, and even complaint before God and then work toward a place of praise and thanksgiving instead of from it.

Over the next few days, I want to take you on the journey of working from lament towards a place of praise.

Look up the definition of lament in a dictionary. (An online dictionary works too!) Write it out here word for word. Below that, write it out in your own words.

I think one of the greatest hindrances to prayer and God's people even wanting to pray is thinking we have to start with a thankful or praiseworthy statement on our lips. But I want you to pause for a moment and think: When you have time set aside to pray, or even think about beginning to pray, what is usually the state of your heart? What part of your story or your day usually needs to come up and out so you can move toward God in a place of trust and see things through a different lens, the lens of thankfulness and praise?

Circle any words that describe where your heart is today, and what would come up and out if you were to pray right now.

Weariness

Loneliness

Worry about finances

Guilt over sin

Relational strain

Debilitating sickness

Doubts about the existence or goodness or God

Failure in your present

Failures from your past

Fear about the future

Worry about the safety or security of your children or the people you love

Unforgiveness toward someone who has hurt you deeply

Grief or sadness over the loss of someone you love

Anger over injustice

Sadness over the change of a certain season in your life

Other:

____

How does knowing it's okay to start with the lament, worry, fear, doubt, loneliness, or complaint instead of praise change your thoughts about prayer and your desire to pray?

To see a Biblical lament in action, read Psalms 42 and 43 in your Bible.

These psalms are two parts of a closely knit poem. Psalm 42:5, 11 and Psalm 43:5 echo the same refrain. It is the refrain of lament—a lament of a worshiper who lived far away from Jerusalem where God's temple and presence dwelled. He longed to be in close proximity once again to God's house and God's people and was lamenting the loss of a season, change, and the felt, near presence of God.

Look at the first three verses of Psalm 42. How does the psalmist open this song or prayer?

Now look at how both Psalms end. Write out the last refrain of both.

Friends, that is the goal of all our praying, lamenting, and complaining. It is not to stay stuck; it is to move toward God. There are only two psalms in the entire psalter that end in total despair or sorrow (which shows us there are times that kind of sorrow or despondency is part of how we process life as well). But the rest of the psalms—148 of them—end in hope, thanksgiving, praise.

Might I suggest the reason these psalms end in praise is because the psalmists were honest enough to start with lament? We cannot heal from something we refuse to remember. We cannot change if we refuse to admit there is anything wrong in the first place. Before we learn anything else, we must learn to be honest when we go to God in prayer so our hearts are ready to heal.

Find the seven components of a lament in Scripture, specifically the Psalms, by looking back at chapter ten in your book. Write them out. Then, we'll look at where to find each element in Psalms 42–43.

1. The Psalm is addressed to God. (See Psalm 42:1–2; 43:1–2a.)
2.
3.
4.
5.
6.
7.

Draw a circle around or put a star by the third component. This is to remind you that Biblical laments do not have to include all seven components, but the one component they do include is complaint.

Now, reread Psalms 42–43 and next to each component, write down the Scripture reference where you see each one. I've done the first one for you. Some verses will be used in more than one component.

Look carefully at the verses you listed by the third component: a complaint. What are some of the complaints the psalmist made here?

Does the psalmist's freedom to express those complaints to God surprise you? Why or why not? If so, which ones surprise you the most?

Does it surprise or comfort you to know the psalmist was complaining about things like perceived rejection by God (Psalm 42:9); the deceitful, unfair, and unjust actions of others (Psalm 43:1–2); and sorrow over a change in circumstances or season of life (Psalm 42:4)? Explain.

Our complaints, doubts, fears, sorrows, or accusations to God about forgetting us or rejecting us do not take God by surprise or throw Him off course. He knows what to do with them all. He stands ready and waiting for us to get the things that weigh us down off our chests and into the light of His presence. We are not strong enough or capable enough to carry the heavy load of life; God alone is.

Amid all the complaints and hurts, depression, and sorrow, Psalm 42:8 stands as a beacon of hope in the middle of it all. Fill in the blanks to complete the verse.

By day the LORD commands his ______________________,
and at night his ______________________ is with me,
a ______________________ to the God of my life.

At the center of every lament, either a lament in Scripture or a lament of your own making is this great reality: No matter what you and I feel, the truth is that God is commanding His steadfast love to cover and uphold our lives. No matter what you and I feel with our hearts, see with our eyes, or hear with our ears, He is singing His song of love, hope, comfort, and life over us. This song has the power to redeem our past, restore our present, and rebuild our future. Our job is to pray—and never stop praying. To knock and never stop knocking. To seek and never stop seeking the God of our life, the Great Shepherd of the sheep who will wipe away every tear from our eyes and turn every lament of our hearts one day to praise (Revelation 7:16–17).

Respond

Father,
Teach me to lament so my heart is open and free to heal and to change. No matter what I feel today, help me to live from the reality and through the lens that Your steadfast love is with me and Your song is sung over me through every dark night, every step of the way.

DAY 3

Read

Today's Personal Study refers to chapter 11 of the book, "How to Lament."

Reflect

In our journey of learning how to pray persistently, honestly, and openly with the purpose of moving toward earned secure attachment, yesterday we looked at why we lament and at the different components of a lament, using Psalm 42–43 as our guide.

Today, I want you to do something a little riskier that may feel a little more vulnerable—I want you to write your own lament.

For those of you like me who are quiet, shy, introverted, and deep feelers, writing a lament might feel as natural as breathing. But for others of you, writing a lament might feel as foreign as learning Greek.

Regardless of your comfort level with lament, it's an important language to learn because Scripture promises: "In the world you *will* have tribulation. But take heart; I have overcome the world" (John 16:33, emphasis mine). In this world you will have trouble— not might or maybe. But will. And the time to learn how to lament, how to process the trouble and hurt and heartache that inevitably comes our way, is in the here and now. It's in our seasons of stability. If we wait to learn how to lament or why it's important to lament in our seasons of struggle, it will be too late—or at the very least, it'll be a great deal harder than if we learn right now.

So even if you don't have something heavy or deep to lament over right now in this season of your life, it's okay. You can pick an issue to process from your past or something not as pressing from your present. So, let's start this process slowly and go step-by-step.

Read Psalm 143. We looked at this psalm in Week 1, but this time, we'll view it through the lens of a lament.

Before we do, look back at yesterday's personal study to review the seven components of lament.

Now, turn in your books to chapter eleven, "How to Lament." The final section of that chapter is "Making Biblical Laments Our Own," and listed in that section are six components of how we, like David, lament. While these six components are like the seven components listed above, they are modeled from Psalm 143.

Take a moment to write them out. Then, next to each one, list the verse or verses in Psalm 143 where you see it used. Some verses may be listed for more than one component. I've done the first one for you.

1. We cry out to God because of His righteousness, not our own. (See Psalm 143:1–2.)
2.
3.
    a.
    b.
4.
5.
6.

As we learn to lament, this last component is vital for us to remember. Yes, we ask for God's justice and deliverance when wrong has been done, but like David, we leave it all in God's hands. The moment we begin to take justice into our own hands and pay back our enemies—evil for evil—is the moment we get into serious trouble. The same evil that exists in our enemies begins to grow in us. Our job is to pray for our enemies while remembering the sinful state and tendencies of our very own souls. Like David, we pray from a place of mercy and humility, asking God to move and act in our lives and in the lives of others because of His righteousness, not our own.

Now, I want you to make this lament your own. Think through something you need to lament right now. Perhaps it's something you've pushed down or buried from the past, but its effects keep popping up in your present. Or perhaps it's something you are going through right now.

What is it you want or need to lament today?

Now, pray through the six components found in David's lament in Psalm 143 step-by-step.

Step 1: Cry Out to God Because of His Righteousness, Not Your Own
Psalm 143:1–2
If you get stuck, start with something like "I cry out to you because You are the God who hears." Seek forgiveness for the areas where you fall short.

Step 2: Complain
Psalm 143:3–4
Be as honest as you can before the Lord; remember, total transparency before Him is the safest place to be.

Step 3a: Remember God's Saving Acts in World History

Psalm 143:5

Choose one or two specific acts of God's deliverance in Scripture, read and remember the specific details of those acts, and turn them into a prayer of thanksgiving and remembrance in the space below.

Step 3b: Remember God's Saving Acts in Your Personal History

Psalm 143:5

Remember at least 2–3 specific incidents of God's saving acts and provision in your life and write them out as a testimony and prayer of thanksgiving in the space below.

Step 4: Ask for God's Presence

Psalm 143:6–8

Use the verses above as a guide and ask for God to be near to you in your sorrow, suffering, and hurt. If you get stuck, ask specifically that you could hear His voice, feel the comfort of His love, and know the direction He wants you to go, even in your pain.

If you need help remembering of some of God's saving acts, consider:

- His deliverance of His people from slavery in Egypt through the Passover in Exodus 12
- the parting of the Red Sea in Exodus 14
- the fall of the walls of Jericho in Joshua 6
- David's defeat of Goliath and the Philistines in 1 Samuel 17
- the miraculous deliverance from the Assyrians in Isaiah 36–37
- Jesus's feeding of the 5000 in Matthew 14
- Jesus's raising of Lazarus from the dead in John 11
- Jesus's death on the cross and resurrection from the grave in Luke 23–24

Step 5: Ask for God's Justice and Deliverance

Psalm 143:9–10

Ask God for deliverance and protection from the evil one and from the enemies of your heart that would keep you far from Him—enemies like anger, hate, unforgiveness, bitterness, and envy. In this portion of your lament, it is okay to be honest with God about the effects of evil on you and the people you love. Just remember that justice belongs to God—our part is to do God's will and obey, leaving justice in His hands.

Step 6: Leave It All in God's Hands

Psalm 143:11–12

In your cries for deliverance, as you leave justice in God's hands, part of that process is forgiving your enemies and asking God for the supernatural strength to do so. If you need help in forming the words or even with the desire to forgive, Romans 12:14–21 is a great place to start.

To continue the practice of writing your own laments to process pain, grief, or just the circumstances of a tough day, I've provided a free printable worksheet with prompts to do so at **susannahbaker.com/freetools.**

Well done, friends. The work you just did was hard but good. It's hard to be honest, really honest, about what we believe about the Lord, our circumstances, and His willingness or desire to act. It's hard to be honest about our complaints before God, and it's hard to want His presence more than we want His deliverance. But learning to lament is lancing the wounds that fester and grow in our hearts, stepping out from the shadows into the light, and beginning the journey of honesty, trust, healing, and growth.

Most days, my lamenting looks more like remembering my day and being honest about the state of my heart. I take five minutes or so to start my prayer time by journaling and being transparent before the face of God.

One final thing: I want you to consider reading your lament aloud to someone you trust. This is an important part of learning to build earned secure attachment. That someone might be your counselor, your spouse, a mentor, or a trusted friend. Telling your story out loud to someone with flesh on, who can listen empathetically and say back to you, "Thank you for sharing that; I'm sorry for your pain, and I love you," can be such a powerful agent of healing in our lives.

Take a moment to pray and think—is there someone on your heart to read your lament aloud to? Write out their name here:

Now take action today, reach out to that person, and set up a time to "lament." Healing is waiting.

Respond

Father,
Thank You for the gift of lament. Thank You for never asking us to dress up and pretend to be anyone other than who we really are. Please give me the courage and honesty to process things transparently before You and to want the guidance and restorative power of Your presence in my life at any cost, even if it means remembering things that are hurtful or hard or surrendering things I want to take into my own hands. With every lament, let me lean more into Your faithful, steadfast love.

Continuing the Calm

The work of lamenting is so good for our souls. As you go about your day, you may notice lingering feelings of sadness mixed with in the joy of being able to praise God in your sadness. If you find yourself wanting to connect further with the Lord, or if there are things too difficult to let go of just yet, I encourage you to try the following additional activity.

Go outside and find a rock or several rocks, however many might represent the sorrows you are thinking through today. On each rock, write a word or symbol (as best you can) that represents each sorrow. Keep an extra rock, the one you like best, for later.

Now consider going on a walk and taking your rocks with you. If you have woods nearby, or a park or trail—or, even better, a lake or pond—go to this place. In your place of solitude, pray over each rock as you walk, sit, or stand. Talk to the Lord about what this rock means to you. As you are ready, throw that rock as far as you dare. (Please take time to notice nearby property that may be unwise to destroy.) But find a good target, aim, and cast that care far away from yourself and into the Lord's hands, symbolized by an empty place in the forest, off the trail, lake, or whatever space you have chosen. While you do so, think about "casting all your anxieties on him, because he cares for you" (1 Peter 5:7).

Now take your remaining rock. What does God, our beautiful Replacer, promise to give in return for your sadness? Write what He has for you on this rock. If you need help, read Isaiah 61:1–3. This rock is for you to keep. You may find there are days that the other rocks find their way back into your spirit, and that's okay. It's one more chance to give them to God again, and His hands are open as many times as you need them to be. But this rock stays. Keep it as a reminder of His promise from His Word to you, His child. It may be hard to believe today or tomorrow but keep praying that the truth of what God has promised will take root in your heart.

DAY 4

Read

Today's Personal Study refers to chapter 12 in the book, "Restoring Through Praise."

Reflect

In our journey of learning how to pray persistently and restoratively, we often begin with lament, especially if we are walking through dark or difficult season. But our goal is to end in praise. Like I shared earlier this week, while we don't always move from a place of praise, our goal is to move toward it.

The primary tool we have to help us do that is God's Word. In God's Word, we find the story of how God moved in the lives of His people in the past and His promises of how He is committed to moving in the present and future. As people who are working toward the goal of earned secure attachment, it is imperative for us to know we can trust the consistency, reliability, and character of our primary caretaker—our Father God. While our circumstances don't always give us reason to praise, His unchanging character and the ways He promises to move in our lives do. So, today and tomorrow, let's spend some time looking at just a few of the reasons we always have to praise our faithful God, no matter what season we are walking through.

Within the book of Psalms, there are more laments than traditional psalms of thanksgiving or praise. But here is the beautiful thing: while there are more laments at the beginning of the book, there are more hymns of praise towards the end. So, in other words, the praise overtakes the laments! Worshipers leave the literary sanctuary of the Psalms with the deep sense of knowing that God turns our "wailing into dancing" (Psalm 30:11 NIV), He comforts all who mourn (Isaiah 61:2), and the end of our stories isn't lament—it's praise. While the end goal of our life is to work and move toward praise, the goal of each of our times of prayer is to work toward praise as well.

Spoiler alert: this can take a long time to learn how to do, especially if you are starting to pray from a place of insecure attachment. I tell you this not to discourage you but to give you hope. I began my prayers with lament for a long time—probably three or four years. I had a lot of sorrow, rejection, anger, and fear of abandonment to get up and out of my soul. But while I started in lament, through using the tool of God's Word—specifically the Psalms—I learned how to let the character of God and the ways He moved in the past and promised to move in my present and future begin to heal and restore the lens through which I saw all of life.

For the very first time, I began to really enjoy praise. I genuinely looked forward to it because it brought such comfort to my soul as I worked through all my insecurities and fears.

I don't know where you are in your journey, and like me, you might have a lot of lamenting to do. But do not despair; beginning in praise will come. Not just because I say so, but because God's Word says so. Our stories are destined to end in praise.

Today and tomorrow, I want to show you a few of the characteristics of God as my Father that consistently brought me comfort and praise as I worked through my laments. I pray they bring you consistent comfort and hope as well.

Read Psalm 84:11–12.

What two things did the psalmist compare God to (v. 11)?

What two things does He give or "bestow" His people?

What does the sun do? How could those things be compared to what God does?

What does a shield do? How could those things be compared to what God does?

In one version of Scripture, verse 11 says, "the Lord gives grace and glory" (NASB). In other words, like a shield, God gives grace. He represents "all that is protective" and is our "answer to fear and defeat."[19] But God is also like the sun and gives glory. He represents all that is "outgoing and positive," life-giving and good, and is our answer to the goodness, light, and life we crave.[20]

But it was in the latter part of verse 11 and in verse 12 that I found the medicine for my healing.

No good thing does He withhold
from those who walk uprightly.
O LORD of Hosts,
blessed is the one who trusts in you!

In the verses above:

- underline the thing God promises to never withhold
- circle the word that describes what brings blessing

Over the years, many of my laments flowed from the fact that I had messed up—again. In my sin and insecure attachment, again I had created conflict. Again, I had feared rejection. Again, I had tried to stabilize and secure myself on unstable people. Again, I had a sabotaged a moment of peace or joy with my husband or kids in my drive toward perfectionism or fear of losing control.

But as I lamented, repented, and put on the new lens of the restorative hope and healing found in God's Word, the promise and praise that met me again and again was this: "no good thing does He withhold from those who walk uprightly. Blessed is the one who trusts in you."

Here was the praise: I couldn't mess my life up permanently, something I feared deeply. The goodness God promised wasn't given to me based on my performance; it was given to me based on the righteousness of Jesus Christ. And my healing didn't depend on my ability to do life perfectly; it depended on my willingness to trust God. Did you catch that? The last line of verse 12 could be translated as: "blessed is whoever is trusting in you."[21] As I trusted that if God was for me, who could be against me; as I trusted His goodness wasn't dependent on my righteousness but His Son's; as I trusted that no good thing would He withhold from those whose walk was blameless; and as I trusted that the blessed person was the trusting person, not the perfect person, I could end my laments in praise.

Psalm 84:11–12 became the anthem and refrain to my life. It began to dig up the lie that I could permanently mess things up and replace it with the truth that I could not mess up or miss out on God's plan for my life. Those truths all gave me reason to praise.

What about you? What are some of the most common or repeated laments in your life or that you start your prayers with?

What truth or truths from Psalm 84:11–12 could turn those laments into praise?

Respond

Father,

How thankful I am to know the goodness You give doesn't depend on me, but on You. Thank You for being a sun and a shield, for giving me Your goodness and glory to heal my shame and Your grace to forgive my sin. No matter how long it takes, teach me to turn my laments into praise. Lead me along paths of righteousness for Your Name's sake. I trust You as my Good Shepherd who restores my soul.

DAY 5

Read

Today's Personal Study refers to chapter 12 in the book, "Restoring Through Praise."

Reflect

Today let's continue to learn how to move from a place of lament to a place of praise as we look at who God is and how He promises to move in our lives according to His Word.

Another Psalm that helped me to work my way up and out of my laments into praise is Psalm 16.

Read Psalm 16:1–11.

We have looked at part of this psalm before, but since this whole psalm is brimming with beauty and truth about who God is, let's focus in again on just a few of the verses.

Look carefully at verses 1–2 and write verse 2 in the space below. Underline the phrase, "I have no good apart from you."

What happens to those who run after other gods (v. 4)?

Because David made God his "chosen portion and [his] cup" (v. 5), how did he view his lot in life (v. 6)?

During my journey of moving toward earned secure attachment, one of the primary things I had to learn was this: God alone is my good. In fact, goodness does not exist apart from Him.

As I lamented my failures, sin, mistakes, and others sins against me, this truth became a source of great healing for my soul. I began to see that any time I tried to take my own goodness into my own hands, secure myself on someone else in my life that I loved, hold onto unforgiveness, or refuse to extend the mercy and grace I had been given to someone else, things didn't end well. No matter how good or justified my plans or patterns seemed in my head, my only good was found in obedience to the Lord, trusting in His Word and His ways. And this gave me great reason to praise, which brings us to the second cause for praise.

Look at verses 8–9 and circle the word "secure."

I have set the LORD always before me;
because He is at my right hand, I shall not be shaken.
Therefore my heart is glad, and my whole being rejoices;
my flesh also dwells secure.

How often did David say he set the Lord before him?

Because God was at David's right hand—a place of strength, help in decision-making, power, and authority—what did David say would not happen?

Because the Lord occupied the place of prominence in David's life, how did his heart, whole being, and flesh respond?

Friends, the second reason I found in this psalm to praise was this: In God alone, I could be secure.

I spent my whole life searching for security. As I have shared before, I wrote an entire prayer guide that I titled *Secure* before I even knew the term "secure attachment" existed. But security itself always felt just out of reach. I believed I was too faulty, too broken, too emotional, too sinful, too insecure, too divisive, too argumentative, and too irrational to ever deserve security or move to a permanently secure place. But not according to God's Word. The only reason I was insecure was not because I was so bad, but because I was looking for other people and things to secure me instead of God Himself.

In one of the hardest seasons of my life, God allowed separation between me and someone I loved dearly. Every lie I had ever thought about myself, I was tempted to believe was true. But in that painful place, God brought about some of the greatest healing and restoration I have ever known—He became my secure place. It was as if He allowed the earthly security I had always craved to fall out from under me so I could literally feel how I had been placing my feet on the unstable ground of other people's approval and affections. But in His kindness, as He removed their presence, He placed my feet on solid ground, which gave me great reason to praise.

Reread Psalm 40:1–3 and review what we learned about it in Week 1.

When we are knee deep in a miry pit, unable to move, unable to save ourselves, and simply stuck and waiting on God, we often think waiting on God means passively sitting there and possibly pouting. But Psalm 40:1 implies that David's waiting involved crying out. Lamenting. Beating the door of heaven down. So, our deliverance and healing don't require us getting our act together, praying perfect prayers, or memorizing a lot of bible verses. It requires us to do one thing: cry out.

And at the perfect time, in the perfect way, God moved. He delivered David out of his lament into security and praise. Throughout Scripture, stepping on a rock often symbolizes placing saving trust and faith in Jesus Christ, our cornerstone (1 Peter 2:4). So as God moved David out of the pit and placed all his steps, security, and stability, on the rock of His presence, He pointed forward to the person and presence of Jesus Christ Himself. As this happened, David began to praise and others around him began to change as well.

The third reason I found in the Psalms to praise was: as I moved toward a place of earned secure attachment, I could trust others around me would begin to a similar place as well.

Like I mention in the book, research affirms the truth the Scriptures declare—when you begin to move toward a place of earned secure attachment, the people closest to you begin to heal and move in that direction as well. And that, my friends, gives us great reason to praise.

Go back and read through three reasons to praise that we find in the psalms:

1. *Our goodness is not dependent on our performance, success, or others' approval. God alone is our good.*
2. *Our security is not dependent on the stability of our circumstances or other people. In God alone, we can be secure.*
3. *As we move toward a place of earned secure attachment, we can trust that God in His time and His way will begin to move others around us as well.*

As you think about these three reasons, how could each one turn a lament in your life to a praise?

If you still have a hard time praising, if you still feel stuck in the pit of insecurity and lament, take heart. Deliverance is coming. Your part is to wait, keep lamenting, keep trusting, keep crying out. At the perfect time, you can be confident of this: deliverance is coming. God will put a new song in your mouth of praise and those around you will praise Him as well.

Respond

Father,

I often want a quick fix and quick deliverance. But Your ways are so different than mine. Bit by bit, slowly but surely, over time, move my heart up and out of the pit of insecure attachment and lament to praise. Set my feet on the solid rock of Your presence. Remind me often that I have no good apart from You. Reign me in when I chase after other gods and teach me how to set You before me always—in every decision I make and emotion I feel. Thank You that deliverance is coming and that praise is the language of my true country. Teach my heart to speak that language as I move closer and closer to my true home.

WEEK 5

Rebuilding the Senses, Part 1

- Like many of us -
Moses had a "shadow" side -

- wells in scripture often represent
an invitation to restore.

- God needed a humble
leader. It took 40 years
of wilderness to get Moses
there...

VIEWER GUIDE: WEEK 5

MAKING GOD OUR HOME

PSALM 90:1–17
EXODUS 2–3:10

- "Lord, ___you___ have been our dwelling place in all generations. Before the mountains were brought forth, or ever you had formed the earth and the world, from everlasting to everlasting ___you___ are God." Psalm 90:1–2
    - This is the key for anyone who wants to become a man or woman of God: ___God___ must become our dwelling place. He must become our parent, our primary caretaker, our ___home___.
    - Like with Moses, God draws us out of the ___waters___, out of the turbulent, chaotic, unpredictable places in our past and present, and sets our feet on the solid rock of His ___presence___.
- "You have set our secret ___sins___ in the light of your ___presence___." Psalm 90:8
    - The ___wilderness___ is the tool God uses to bring us to the end of ourselves, to let our secret sins come into the light of His presence, and to have the margin to make God our home.

- Every wilderness season God allows has a well, an invitation to allow God's presence, guidance, and friendship in our lives to become more real than anyone else's.

- "So teach us to number our days that we may get a heart of wisdom." Psalm 90:12
    - We need the wisdom to stay humble enough to own who we really are and dependent enough on making God alone our refuge, safe place, and home.
    - If we let the wilderness God has allowed to do its work, we will begin to hear the quiet, persistent, life-changing, identity-altering voice of God.

- We will begin to have the margin to hear God's voice, to stay attuned to His presence, and to be responsive to His call on our lives.

Video Sessions available at susannahbaker.com/biblestudies

– the mountain of God, Mt. Horeb, is in the middle of nowhere.

Wisdom: not less-than morals

– to train our senses to listen.

– Solitude must do its good work.

– When Moses took things into his own hands, it led to murder!

PERSONAL STUDY

Before beginning this week's study, please read chapters 13–15 of the book.

DAY 1

Read

Today's Personal Study refers to chapter 13, "The Foundation of the Senses."

Reflect

It's surprising that the way we begin to rebuild relationship with God as our primary caretaker is through our senses. But it's true. Just like a parent builds a foundation for relationship with their newborn baby through the senses, so does God as our parent build the same foundation for us.

The problem is that the fall, sin, and the curse destroyed our spiritual senses; sin darkened our eyes so we cannot see God. It stopped up our ears so we cannot hear God. It crushed us with its tightening grip so we cannot feel God's nurturing touch. It filled our mouths with bitterness so we cannot taste God's goodness, and it covered us with the stench of death so we cannot clothe ourselves with God's resurrecting life.

Our senses don't need a simple makeover; they need resurrection.

But, as always, God provides.

Read Ephesians 2:1–10.

Look closely at verses 1–3. Before God "raised us up with him and seated us with him in the heavenly places" (v. 6), what was our spiritual state or condition?

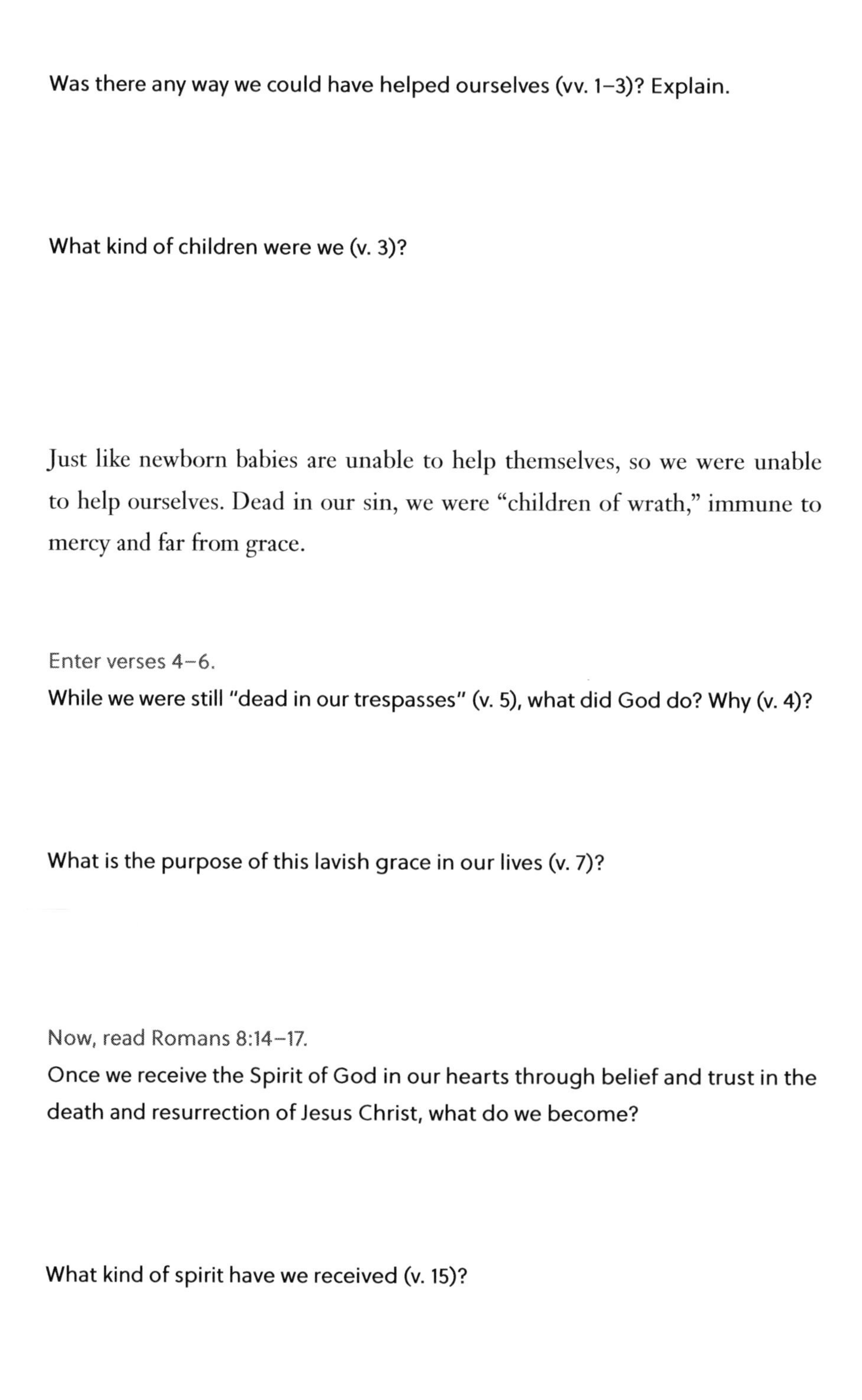

Was there any way we could have helped ourselves (vv. 1–3)? Explain.

What kind of children were we (v. 3)?

Just like newborn babies are unable to help themselves, so we were unable to help ourselves. Dead in our sin, we were "children of wrath," immune to mercy and far from grace.

Enter verses 4–6.

While we were still "dead in our trespasses" (v. 5), what did God do? Why (v. 4)?

What is the purpose of this lavish grace in our lives (v. 7)?

Now, read Romans 8:14–17.

Once we receive the Spirit of God in our hearts through belief and trust in the death and resurrection of Jesus Christ, what do we become?

What kind of spirit have we received (v. 15)?

By the Spirit, what do we cry out? Why is this important?

In Aramaic, the language Jesus spoke, "Abba" means "Father," or even more specifically than that, "Daddy." It's what little children use to call on the help, name, and love of their fathers.

Friends, this changes everything. We were children of wrath, who were dead in our trespasses, but God—because of how much He loves us—rescued you. He ran a daring Good Friday mission, busted into the orphanage of sin and hell itself, and brought you out from death, abandonment, and the stench of sin, into life, adoption, and the fragrance of resurrection life.

And in a moment, through relationship with Christ, you became a child of God.

But here is the part that is both hard and glorious part all wrapped into one: while our transformation from orphaned to adopted took a moment, our becoming a child takes a lifetime. We have to unlearn all of our orphan habits, behaviors, and ruts and learn to walk the path of trust and obedience as a beloved child of God. This work happens through the transformation of our spiritual senses every day.

Reread Psalm 23:3. What is the emphasis of restoration? In other words, while we are living here on this earth, what does God promise to restore?

For our souls to be restored, we need to work on knowing God and being known through our spiritual senses. Every day, we must do the work of learning to hear God's voice with the ears of hearts and trust Him enough to obey.

We must learn to see God with the eyes of our hearts and allow the reality of who He is and what He promises to do to be greater than anything we see in our external circumstances.

We must learn to sense what it feels like to be steadied by God's hand alone and turn away from any other influence that leads us to insecurity and ruin. We must learn to taste the goodness of whatever meal God places before us, trusting that He knows exactly what to give us, when to give it, and that it will lead to our ultimate good. And we must learn to clothe ourselves every day with the robes of Christ, robes scented with mercy, healing for our wounds, and resurrection life. It is this aroma we must carry out to a world in need, crushed by death, sin, and its consequences.

This spiritual hearing, seeing, touching, tasting, and smelling takes a lifetime—a lifetime of sermons, time in God's Word, time on our knees in prayer processing through doubt, wrestling, and questions, all the while choosing to trust and wait.

This is why the most effective, powerful prayer we can pray on a regular basis for ourselves and the people we love is the prayer the apostle Paul prayed for the church in Ephesus.

Read Ephesians 1:15–19.

What did Paul pray for the believers in Ephesus (v. 17)?

What did he ask the Spirit to do? Fill in the blanks (v. 18).

[have] the ____________________ of your ____________________

____

Notice Paul did not ask for the circumstances to change in the lives of the people he loved so much; he asked for the vision of their hearts to change. Why?

List the three specific things Paul pray would come from this enlightened vision in their hearts (vv. 18–19).

Friends, this is my exact prayer for you. Over the next three weeks we have together, I am praying that the eyes of your heart are enlightened to know and to see the immeasurable riches, the secure identity, and the greatness of the power you have been given as a child of God. My prayer is that through this knowledge, you grow up and out of orphan behaviors into the confidence and secure attachment that is rightfully yours as a beloved, adopted, child of God.

Response

Father,

Thank You for loving me enough to save me from my sin when I could do nothing to save myself. Thank You that through Christ, I am an orphan no longer; I am a beloved child of God. Over the next three weeks, please begin to rebuild the foundation of my senses and through Your Word and Your Spirit. Father, restore my soul.

DAY 2

Read

Today's Personal Study refers to chapter 14 in the book, "Hearing."

Reflect

For the next three days, I want to spend time in God's Word, learning how to apply the truths we covered in chapter fourteen about our spiritual sense of hearing. To know what we need to work on or adjust with our spiritual hearing, let's remember the truths about how a securely attached child hears, trusts, and obeys.

- A securely attached child uses their voice to cry out and tell their parent what they need, believing the parent will respond and has the desire and the resources to meet their need.
- A securely attached child is comforted by the parent's presence when they come. The parent's presence does not produce fear, stress, worry, or anxiety in the child but great comfort and peace.
- A securely attached child can trust and obey the parent's answer to their cry, even if the answer is "no" or contrary to what the child wants. It doesn't mean the child doesn't have questions, doubts, confusion, or sorrow about their parent's response, but it does mean the child can trust the parent's response is for their good.

Take a moment and think long and hard about those indicators of a securely attached child. How do you respond to God as your good Father and primary caretaker in those three areas? Be as honest as you can in your answers to the following questions.

Do you regularly use your voice to cry out and tell Him your needs?

- If so, was there ever a time when you didn't feel like you could? Explain.

- If not, why not? Do you believe He doesn't care or isn't listening? Or do you believe He lacks the resources—either the goodness, character, or power—to give you what you needed? Explain.

If you are comfortable using your voice and crying out to God, are you able to receive comfort through God's Word and the presence of His Spirit within you?

- If not, why not? If so, how did you get to this place of comfort?

- Is the promise and assurance of His presence enough to stabilize and secure you, or does His presence make you fearful, uncomfortable, unsettled, or even resentful and angry? Explain.

Are you able to trust and obey what God tells you?

- If God tells you no, are you able to obey His answer through His Word, or do you go ahead and do whatever you want to do? Explain.

- Or maybe you can obey His no, but struggle obeying with an attitude of trust. Do you struggle with having long periods of resentment, anger, bitterness, or unforgiveness if God doesn't give you what you are asking for? Explain.

If you consistently and regularly struggle with any of these indicators of a securely attached child, I want you to think about why. In other words, where do these attitudes and behaviors come from?

Remember, if you were not securely attached to your primary caretaker as a child and have not actively worked on earned secure attachment to God as an adult, then walking securely in your relationships with God, your spouse, children, friends, or any other significant relationship in your life will be extremely difficult.

So, let's think about those questions in the context of our relationship to our parents or primary caretakers.

Did you regularly use your voice to cry out to your parents and tell them your needs?

- If so, was there ever a time when you didn't feel like you could? Explain.

- If not, why not? Do you believe your parents didn't care or weren't listening? Or did you believe your parents lacked the resources—either the goodness, character, or power—to give you what you needed? Explain.

If you were comfortable using your voice and crying out, were you comforted when your parents came and responded to you? In other words, when they came, was their presence enough to stabilize and secure you? Or did their presence make you fearful, uncomfortable, unsettled, or even resentful and angry? Explain.

Once your parents responded, were you able to trust and obey what they told you to do?

- If your parents told you no, were you able to obey their answer, or did you go ahead and do whatever you wanted to do? Explain.

- Or maybe you were able to obey their no, but you struggled obeying with an attitude of trust. Did you struggle with prolonged periods of resentment, anger, bitterness, or unforgiveness if your parents didn't give you what you were asking for?

After thinking about your responses to your parents, in what ways are you able to see a little more clearly perhaps why you struggle with secure attachment to God through hearing?

Perhaps you were securely attached to your parents as a child, but a significant trauma occurred in your adult life, disrupting that secure attachment and the way you trusted and related to God as your good Father.

If that is you, then what significant events in your life contribute to your unwillingness or inability to use your voice and cry out to God, feel comfort and peace through the presence of God's Spirit and Word, and do what He tells you to do with a willing and trusting heart?

As we close our time of study today, choose one of these passages from Psalm 34 to read and answer the questions that follow.

- If you struggle with crying out to God, read Psalm 34:4–6, 17–19
- If you struggle is mainly with feeling comfort when God shows up, read Psalm 34:8–10.
- If your struggle is predominantly with trusting and obeying what God tells you to do, read Psalm 34:12–17.

How do the verses you chose help answer, resolve, and heal your struggle and fear?

What lie have you believed about God that you need to replace with the truth found in God's Word? Explain.

What one thing from those verses sticks with you about the character of God and your response as His securely attached child?

Respond

Father,
So often, we are afraid of crying out to You because we fear You will not come, do not care, or lack the resources to provide. We are not comforted by Your presence because we doubt Your consistent goodness, power to provide, and love. We do not want to trust and obey because we are used to figuring out life on our own and doing what we want, when we want to do it. But God, the truth of Your Word changes everything. When we cry out to You, You always respond to us. Our faces become radiant as You lift off our shame and supply us with the goodness of Your presence. Obedience to Your Word always ends in goodness and life. Rewrite the narrative of our lives and secure our hearing to You as we learn to cry out, receive, trust and obey.

DAY 3

Read

Today's Personal Study refers to chapter 14 in the book, "Hearing."

Reflect

Yesterday we started to rebuild the foundation of earned secure attachment by looking at the sense of hearing. To continue with the journey, we move from remembering the ruins of the past to restoration.

Like we learned about at the end of Week 3 and beginning of Week 4, Jesus gave His disciples an example of how to pray and in doing so, gives us insight into the restorative process of the soul.

A large part of His example and instruction on prayer to His disciples has to do with forgiveness—asking forgiveness from God for our own sin and then forgiving others for the sin they have committed against us.

Read Matthew 6:9–15, focusing on verses 12, 14–15.

Describe what Jesus taught His disciples to pray in verse 12.

In verses 14–15, He explained why forgiving others for their sin against us is so important. Write out Jesus's explanation in your own words.

When taken into context with the rest of Scripture, what we can understand from Jesus's words is this: We do not earn our Father's forgiveness. Our forgiveness of others is the proof that we ourselves have understood and received the forgiveness of the Father.

We know we don't "earn" anything with the Lord—all we are given, forgiveness included, is grace. But if we hold tightly onto our grudges, refusing to forgive, it is proof that we don't understand the extent of what we ourselves have been forgiven. Anything we could hold against another pales in comparison to what God could hold against us. When we extend grace to others, we show we understand who we really are in relation to a holy God.

God wants us to forgive others because He knows in doing so, we release the debts that would rot our souls if we continued to hold onto them. He also knows one of the greatest ways we open ourselves to receiving and experiencing His love for our own hearts is, ironically, by forgiving others. We cannot forgive others unless we look at ourselves honestly and recognize the real sinners we are, while understanding how deeply loved and truly forgiven we are at the same time.

We don't excuse the debts others owe us or say they aren't owed. What we acknowledge is that they are simply not owed to us. We surrender them into much more capable hands than our own.

Read Romans 12:19–21.

Why are we never to avenge ourselves (v. 19)? Who does vengeance belong to?

What is our role with the very people who have hurt us instead (vv. 20–21)?

These are hard words, impossible demands, really, unless we take God at His word and obey Him with the help of His Spirit. Evil isn't overcome with evil. The evil another person has committed against you isn't overcome by you committing evil against them in return. Unforgiveness only gives evil the same free reign to grow inside of you as it has done in that other person. Evil is only overcome by good. The cross of Jesus Christ is proof of that. Sin and evil in our lives were overcome as the only One who was ever fully and completely good died for us while we were still sinners. His goodness overcame our evil and transformed us from children of wrath to children of God (see Ephesians 2:3–5).

With that being said, let's turn to the work of forgiveness today, the first step in restoration. To start, go back and look through your responses to your questions from yesterday concerning God as your parent.

Is there anything you need to repent of to the Lord?

- Have you stuffed your emotions, refusing to cry out to Him?
- Do you rely too much on your own resources and ability to make it through life without His help as your good Father?
- Do you doubt His goodness and love, thinking He is like your primary caretaker or parents?
- Do you doubt His power and resources to take care of you and answer your cries?
- Do you doubt His desire to move toward you and respond to you every time you cry out?
- Have you made an idol out of His image, worshiping a false image of a god who looks like your earthly parents instead of who God says He is in His Word?
- Have you refused to let His presence bring you consistent comfort, hope, and peace?
- Have you refused to obey His Word once He has made it clear to you, relying on your own wisdom instead of His?
- Have you obeyed but done so with an attitude of resentment or consistent grumbling and complaining?

Circle two or three of the questions above that resonate with you, and then pray through them in this prayer, modifying as needed.

Father,

Please forgive me for __________________. I have doubted who You say You are in Your Word and made You out to be someone or something You are not. I have compared You to my primary caretaker or other people around me like __________________, instead of worshiping You for who You really are. I repent. Restore my hearing, God. Help me use my voice to cry out to You, trusting You will respond with exactly what I need. Help me learn to trust that You always come when I call and to be comforted with the peace Your presence always provides. Help me to learn to obey and do what You say with a trusting, contented heart. Restore my soul, and securely attach me to You through a renewed ability to cry out to You, hear, and obey. In Jesus's Name I pray, Amen.

Now go back and look through your responses to your questions from yesterday concerning your relationship to your parents or primary caretaker. Or think back to a significant trauma in your life that disrupted secure attachment with your primary caretaker.

Is there anyone you need to forgive and anything specific you need to forgive them for?

- Was your parent unavailable to you when you cried out to them in need?
- Were they too bound up by their own emotional hurt and pain to tend to yours?
- Did they lack the resources—either emotional or physical—to give you what you needed?
- Did they respond to you in inappropriate ways—either through overly harsh discipline or emotional or verbal abuse?
- Did they respond to you in inconsistent ways—sometimes they were there and sometimes they were not?
- Did the obedience they demanded come from harsh or unloving motives?

Circle two or three of the questions above that resonate with you, and then pray through them, using the prayer on the following page as a guide.

Father,
I forgive ________________ (my parents, primary caretaker, or someone else connected to a significant trauma) for ________________. While what they did was wrong or evil, evil is not mine to repay. If I continue to hold onto unforgiveness for ________________, the same evil that was in them will continue to grow and fester in me. Vengeance is Your job. My job is to release the debt they owe me into Your wise, capable, just, and loving hands. I am a sinner, just like my parents before me. I want to restore and rebuild walls in my family, not to continue the pattern of tearing them down. As I forgive, give me the grace to honor my parents and to move towars them or their memory in love. As I restore and work on earned secure attachment with You, restore and repair the broken relationships around me.

You've heard me say it before, but I will say it again: that was hard work but good work today. Well done. While forgiveness is some of the hardest heart work we will ever do, it is also some of the most transformative, healing, and freeing.

My prayer for you today is that as you release the genuine debts owed to you, you will be filled with the overflowing, transformative, and freeing goodness, grace, and love of your heavenly Father. You are His beloved child, and your life is secure in His capable hands.

Respond

Father,
I know forgiveness is not a magic wand I wave or magic words I say so all hurt is instantly gone. Forgiveness is a process; it is a long obedience in the same direction. Keep me accountable to continuing to repent for my sin against You when I commit it and to forgiving those who have sinned against me until I am truly free.

Continuing the Calm

The work of forgiveness can be a simple task or a repetitive one. If you are having difficulty forgiving someone, God is not surprised by this. Remember when Jesus said in Matthew 18:22 to forgive someone seventy-seven times? I wonder sometimes if He knew that might be how many times we would have to hand our unforgiveness over for the same trespass against us.

If you are having difficulty letting go of an offense or letting someone off the hook, I encourage you to write them a letter. This is not a letter that must be sent. Rather, it is meant for you to express some or all the hurt you have experienced at their hands. As you write, pray over each hurt, asking God to heal your heart and the heart of the person about whom you are writing.

The second part of the letter can be about your difficulty in forgiving. Maybe you can't quite let go at this moment, so write about that. Write a prayer that God will help you release this once and for all. Maybe you can forgive in this moment but are concerned you will take back the unforgiveness at a later point. Write a commitment to release this person back into the Father's hands any time you realize you are not walking in forgiveness.

The point of this letter is to provide a different way of expressing your thoughts and releasing this person to the Father. If you would like, take the list of offenses, and cut out each one. Notice God's presence with you as you do this. He does not ask you to forgive others on your own but is there to help you. Pray over each strip, and as you do so, tear it up. Release the offense to your Father, your Refuge and Righteous Judge. Let this offering of forgiveness be a fragrant offering to Him.

DAY 4

Read

Today's Personal Study refers to chapter 14 in the book, "Hearing."

Reflect

We have remembered the ways we act like orphans in our hearing instead of like beloved children and started the journey of restoration through repentance. Today, we'll continue that journey through rebuilding our sense of hearing with the tools we know we need and have at our disposal to use: God's Word, prayer, and the Psalms.

To do that, let's use the same pattern of persistent prayer we used last week and apply it here to our spiritual sense of hearing. My hope is that as we do this together today, you will see how you can do this on your own in the future as unhealthy patterns or unhealed places of pain surface in your life. Today is not an end in the journey of restored hearing and earned secure attachment but a beginning.

Persistent Prayer to Rebuild Our Hearing

Step 1: Remember

Look back at Day 2 of this week and identify the main way you act like an orphan instead of a beloved, securely attached child in your relationship with God. Do you stuff your voice, or are you able to cry out? Do you receive consistent comfort and peace through God's Word and God's Spirit, or does His presence make you feel uncomfortable, fearful, resentful, or restless? Do you obey all the way, right away, with a happy heart (as I used to tell my children), or is trusting obedience difficult for you?

Set a timer for five minutes and use the space provided to tell God exactly where you are today. Remember, honesty and transparency with Him is the best place to be.

Step 2: Restore Through God's Word

Now, let's process your life and learn to use your sense of hearing through a different lens, the lens of God's Word.

Reread Psalm 34:4–19.

In Psalm 34, David was drowning in fear and dangerous circumstances. He was fearful for his life. But he didn't stuff his fears and try to meet his own needs, or run to other people for help. What did David do instead (vv. 4, 6)?

What did God do when David sought Him and cried out (vv. 4–6)?

What is God's promise to His people when they cry out to Him (v. 17)?

Look carefully at verse 4. What did God deliver David from? Explain.

What happens to those who act like secure beloved children and look to the Lord (v. 5) and cry out to Him (v. 6)?

Now look carefully at verses 8–10. Every time God's children cry out to Him, what characteristic of God do we taste and see?

When our fear of God becomes greater than any other fear, what are we promised as His children (vv. 9–10)?

Now look closely at verses 11–14. Why is obedience to what God commands so important?

What happens to those who turn away from God, follow their own heart, walk their own way, and disobey Him (v. 16)?

Are godly or righteous people promised protection or immunity from troubles, afflictions, brokenness, or suffering (vv. 18–19)? Explain.

Now let's go back and process our story and sense of hearing again through the lens of God's Word.

Step 3: Praise

Take the truth of what you just read in Psalm 34:4–19, and apply it to the way you cry to God, respond to His presence, or trust and obey His voice. In the space below, insert into your story the reality of God is who He says He is and what He promises to do.

Step 4: Repent

Like we learned yesterday, restoration cannot occur without repentance. In the space below, write out a prayer repenting to God for ignoring His Word and choosing to see the way you cry out, respond to His presence, and make choices about trust and obedience through any lens apart from His Word.

Step 5: Ask

God loves to fulfill the promises He makes in His Word, but He loves for us to ask (remember Luke 11:9–10). Here is where you take the truth of God's Word and use it to help you ask Him to rebuild your sense of hearing to securely connect to Him as His beloved child. Pick one specific promise from Psalm 34:4–19 that resonates with you, and in the space below, write out a prayer asking God to insert the reality of that promise into your life. Ask Him to bring it to your heart and mind often throughout the day.

Coming up with the words to know how to yield to God at the end of our prayers can be difficult. Consider using the following prayer to help you if you get stuck:

Father, the command that jumps out at me today from Your Word is ______________. Let Your Words "spring to my mind, interpreting my moment, guiding my choices, and strengthening my heart."[22] I release these specific worries, fears, or concerns about my day into Your hands: ______________. I receive the promise of Your comfort, help, and steadfast love for all that is ahead. Restore me from the inside out so that I can relate to You as my good Father, believing with my whole heart and showing with my actions that I am Your securely beloved child. In Jesus's name I pray, Amen.

Step 6: Yield

Here is where we allow God to examine our hearts and show us if there is a command for our life or for our day we need to yield to, trust, or obey. Here is where we also release our circumstances, worries, and needs into our Father's hands and receive to the goodness and mercy He promises to give. In the space below, write out a prayer yielding your heart, circumstances, and needs to the Father.

You are on a good and beautiful path to restored hearing with your good Father. In the days ahead, remember to go back to His promises in Psalm 34: cry out to Him with confidence that He hears your voice and will answer; receive the goodness and sufficiency of His presence in your life; and respond in trust and obedience as His beloved child.

Respond

Father,

You who began a good work in me will be faithful to carry it on to completion (Philippians 1:6). Thank You for beginning the good work in me of earned secure attachment with my hearing. Keep my feet on paths of righteousness in the days ahead as I learn to relate to You as Your securely beloved child.

Continuing the Calm

When you think about your toolbox for healing, you might have some questions. Throughout this study, we have been adding different tools, any of which you might access at any time once you have learned them. The main tools are prayer and seeking God in His Word. Other, more specific, tools are the kinds of prayer you have been learning like repentant prayer, restorative prayer, and yielding. Emotional tools are the visualizations and breathing exercises.

Here is a chance to add sense-specific tools. The key to the toolbox is remembering what is actually in there when you need them. Below, write out the following so you will have it in a place you can remember.

- Write out one verse through which you connect closely with God. This might be spoken out loud as you focus on your breathing (we call this a Breath Prayer):

- Write out one prayer you have learned in this study that you might use again in the future:

- Write out one song you love to sing to the Lord (it's up to you whether you do this around other people):

Great job! Make sure to put these tools in a place you will see them often and remember to use them.

DAY 5

Read

Today's Personal Study refers to chapter 15 in the book, "Sight."

Reflect

Now that we have walked through practical steps of what restored hearing looks like, I want to turn our attention to rebuilding our sight. After we learn to hear God's voice, receive comfort from His presence, and trust and obey, we must learn to look up and keep our eyes fixed on our good Father.

Like I mentioned in the book, it matters where we look. If we want to walk a secure path, we must keep our eyes fixed on Jesus who knows exactly what path to lead us down and through.

We have already started some of the work on sight in Week 3, Day 1, so turn back to that day in your workbook, and write the same answer from that day.

If you could sum up in one word the lens through which you most often saw your life, what would it be?

So often, the lens through which we see life doesn't feel like a choice or something we can put on or take off at will; it simply feels like us, part and parcel of who we are. But the fact is that we do have a choice. We can change the direction of our lives by changing the lens through which we see. Changing our lens doesn't mean we can change our circumstances; but it does mean we can change our attitude and *response* to our circumstances. And a different response can change everything.

To change our lens, we have to stop and become aware of not only the lens through which we see things but remember how we got there.

I want you to think how a securely attached child responds to his or her parents through the sense of sight.

- A securely attached child can hold the gaze of their parents in times of appropriate intimacy. They delight in the comfort and nurture an intimate gaze brings and the close relationship between the parent and child it fosters.
- A securely attached child can hold the gaze of their parents during times of discipline, trusting that whatever consequences the parents give are necessary and good.
- A securely attached child is content, calm, and comforted under the gaze of their parents.

Let's look at the first way a securely attached parent and child interact and then think through your own relationship with your parents.

Were you able to hold your parents' gaze during times of appropriate intimate connection? Why or why not?

When you parents looked at you, did you sense delight and joy in their gaze? If not, what did you sense in your parents' gaze? Explain.

What kinds of emotions or feeling did your parents' gaze foster in you?

Perhaps you had a great relationship with your parents and sensed joy and appropriate intimate connection through their gaze, but you still struggle with seeing yourself through a pervasive lens of shame. If that is you, I want you to stop for a moment and think: what was the relationship like between your mom and dad?

The primary way children learn to see themselves is by the way their father sees, treats, and interacts with their mother. Your dad could have loved, respected, and delighted in you but struggled in honoring and delighting in your mom. If that was the case, then chances are, you struggle with seeing yourself through a lens a love, delight, and honor as well.

Be as honest as you can and describe how your dad treated your mom.

Let's stop right here for a moment. Those questions could be really tough to think through or honestly answer for some of you, and for that, I am so sorry. Some of you had parents who were absent, either by choice or through sickness or death, and the lack of their gaze left a huge void in your life. Others of you had parents consistently looked at you with anger, distrust, contempt, or disdain, and the way they saw you is still the lens through which you see yourself and all of life. Others of you were seen through a lens of love and joy by your parents but lived in a household where there was a lack of love between your mom and dad, and that lack still colors the way you still see yourself today.

Let's begin to change that today. Today is the day to tell the enemy of your soul, "Enough!" and to learn to put on the lens of truth and faithful, steadfast love through which your heavenly Father sees you.

Read Psalm 139:1–6.

This might be a familiar psalm to many of you, but I want to read it today through the lens of sensory connection. As you read, ask yourself how your heavenly Father—your primary parent and caretaker—sees you.

Look at verses 1–2. What word did David repeat? Fill in the blanks.
O LORD, you have searched me and ________________ me! You ________________ when I sit down and when I rise up; you discern my thoughts from afar.

This word "know" and its different derivatives are repeated often throughout Psalm 139, and it's a word in the Hebrew that means "to know, to discern, to be acquainted with . . . to be familiar . . . various types of knowledge which are gained through the senses."[23] God's knowledge of us is not just an intellectual knowledge—it's a knowledge based on His sensory interactions with us. And nowhere in Scripture is this made clearer than in Psalm 139. He is the parent and primary caretaker in our lives who sees us, hears us—even our inmost thoughts—and touches, rescues, stabilizes, nourishes, and protects us.

Read verses 13–16. At what point in our lives did His sensory knowledge of us begin? When did He begin to "see" you and take notice and thought of your life?

Now turn to Deuteronomy 32:9–12. In this portion of Scripture, Moses is singing over the Israelites, God's people, and telling them their story or history of rescue and redemption from Egypt and the way God cared for them.

Read verse 10 below and underline everything God did for His people. I've done the first one for you:

"He found him in a desert land,
and in the howling waste of the wilderness;
he encircled him, he cared for him,
he kept him as the apple of his eye."

The "apple of [God's] eye," a phrase echoed throughout Scripture, is literally His pupil, the dead center. As God's people, His rescued and redeemed sons and daughters, we are not in God's peripheral vision, someone or something He thinks about only now and again or if we yell, scream, or cry loud enough. We are at the very center of His vision. He sees all of life through the lens of His loving care for His people.

Let's look at one more place in Scripture to understand how God, our primary parent, sees us.

Read Isaiah 62:2–5.

Once again, the prophet Isaiah was speaking to God's people, telling them the way God saw them, painting a picture of promise and hope for the future.

What did Isaiah say God's people would be called by, and who gave them this name (v. 2)?

Now look at the first part of verse 4: what were the old names of God's people?

Focus on the second part of verse 4: what are our new names?

Look closely at the last part of verse 4: when God looks at you, what emotion or feeling does it evoke in Him?

What is God's rejoicing over you compared to (v. 5)?

Friends, the Scriptures we have just read are the answer to every void, hurt, or past pain we have experienced from a parent's gaze. God is the present parent who knit us together in our mother's womb, saw our unformed substance, delighted in what He saw, and wrote out all our days. As His sons and daughters, we are the very center of His eye; there is not a day that goes by that He forgets about us or ignores our cries for help. And here is the very best part: the prophet Isaiah tells us when God looks at us, the emotion evoked is delight. He rejoices over us like a bridegroom rejoices over His bride.

The truths we read today are the answer and antidote to every void, hurt, or pain we feel from our parents' gaze from the past. These passages are our new lens, a way we must choose to put on over our eyes and see our past, present, and future.

Go back and look at the word you wrote at the beginning of today for the old lens through which you see your life.

With the knowledge you have now from God's Word, what is the new lens you want to learn to see your life? It might be the same word you wrote in Week 3, or it might be a different word after today's personal study.

Can I tell you something? Seeing your life through this new lens will be a choice. It might be the most important choice you make every day for the rest of your days. Learning to see your life through the lens of truth, through the lens of Your Father's gaze instead of your past, is a fight. It requires paying close attention to your thoughts and ways of relating to yourself, God, and other people, and choosing a new path, a new set of glasses, a new name, and a new lens.

But by the grace of God, with the help of God's Spirit inside of us and His Word given to direct and guide us, we can learn to see life through the lens of our good Father one day, one step, one thought, and one choice at a time.

Respond

Father,

I know that restoration starts with repentance, so I repent for choosing to see my life through any other lens outside of the truth found in Your Word. Forgive me for elevating the way I see myself, or the way my parents saw me, above the way you see me. I forgive my parents for the ways they fell short of seeing me through a lens of steadfast love and grace, and I forgive them for the ways they failed to see each other and their marriage through that same lens of love. As I learn to see myself and all of life through your lens of faithful love and delight, enable me to extend that same love to my parents and others around me as well.

WEEK 6

Rebuilding the Senses, Part II

The Good Samaritan

- different race
- costly (money, time, energy)
- not a religious act --

It was a Compassionate act.

– one of Jesus' last miracle before the cross was healing a man's ear.

VIEWER GUIDE: WEEK 6

LEARNING TO SEE

– Can you let God settle your soul when you are disregulated? that is a sign of secure attachment

RECOGNIZING OUR BLINDNESS, ACTS 9:1–19

· Make God an home

- We ___cannot___ see Jesus on our own; true sight is a gift we ___receive___, never anything we earn on our own.
- While we are given sight immediately at our conversion as the children of God, it is also something we must receive ___gradually___ * like Paul, we must learn to see Christ.
  - Sight of Jesus ___transforms___ and ___informs___ everything else.

– ~~Her~~ My transformation is dependent on your willingness to see things through His lens.

LEARNING TO SEE, PHILIPPIANS 3:3–8

- Paul learns to see:
  - The ___worthlessness___ of the flesh
  - The ___worthiness___ of Christ

· the temple had to be destroyed so that His people could be the temple! We would be the place where God's presence would dwell.

CONTINUING TO SEE, 2 CORINTHIANS 12:7–9; EPHESIANS 3:14–19

- The weaknesses in our lives are often the very thing we need to help us continue to see Jesus.
- Through prayer, we continually seek to comprehend Christ's love.
    - We must learn to respond to life not through the lens of our circumstances but through the lens of Christ's love.

Video Sessions available at susannahbaker.com/biblestudies.

* We aren't human "doings". We are human beings. We should focus less on what we do; rather be the person God wants us to be. Then we will do His will.

* The thing that clouds our vision the most is pride. Pride says, "I can do this on my own."

* Our weaknesses are a gift for our soul. Eph. 3:14-19

Chosen Juice

PERSONAL STUDY

Before beginning this week's study, please review chapter 15 and read chapters 16–17 of the book.

DAY 1

Read

Today's Personal Study refers to chapter 15, "Sight."

Reflect

Now that we have identified the old lens through which we see ourselves and some of the reasons *why* we see that way, we must learn, every day, how to put our new lens on—the lens through which we see our heavenly Father and how He sees us.

Refer to the end of your Personal Study from yesterday. What is the new lens through which you want to learn to see God, yourself, and others?

Just like Mia Grace, the greatest work of your life will be learning to see all of life through that lens. In his book, *Life of the Beloved*, Henri Nouwen writes, "If it is true that we not only are the Beloved, but also have to *become* the Beloved. . . . how then can we get a grip on this process of becoming? . . . *Becoming the Beloved means letting the truth of our Belovedness become enfleshed in everything we think, say, or do*. . . . Becoming the Beloved is pulling the truth revealed to me from above down into the ordinariness of what I am, in fact, thinking of, talking about, and doing from hour to hour."[24]

How do we do that? How do we begin to *see* all of our life through this lens of enfleshed Belovedness? Last week, we talked about the first of three indicators of a child securely attached to their parents through the sense of sight. This week, we'll talk about the last two. I've provided all three again for you here.

- A securely attached child can hold their parents' gaze in times of appropriate intimacy. They delight in the comfort and nurture an intimate gaze brings and the close relationship between the parent and child it fosters.
- A securely attached child can hold their parents' gaze during times of discipline, trusting that whatever consequences the parents give are necessary and good.
- A securely attached child is content, calm, and comforted underneath the gaze of their parents.

Let's start by thinking through your relationship with your own parents.

Were you able to hold your parents' gaze during times of discipline or correction? Why or why not?

Were you able to trust the consequences they gave were necessary, just, and good? Explain.

Did the gaze of your parents calm you down and bring you peace? If not, why not?

Were you able to be content in your parents' presence, even if the reality of your circumstances wasn't what you wanted or expected it to be? Explain.

Now think about your relationship with the Lord for a moment. Are you able to hold His gaze, be content in His presence, and accept His no, even if life does not look the way you want it to?

If not, after thinking about your interactions with your parents, are you able to see a little more clearly perhaps why you struggle with secure attachment to God in this area of sight? Explain.

God's Word tells us so many profound things about what happens when we shift our gaze from the circumstances or people around us to the presence of God.

Read Psalm 131:1–3.

In just three short verses, the psalmist painted a helpful picture of what secure attachment and a focused gaze looks like with the Lord.

Where was David not looking (v. 1)?

Where did David tell us his hope, or gaze of his soul, was found (v. 3)?

Look at verse 2. When David chose to take his eyes off his circumstances, or unmet wants or desires, and placed them on the Lord, what words did he use to describe the state of his soul? Circle any words that apply.

calm	childlike	needy
agitated	content	quiet
restless	greedy	unsatisfied
anxious	grasping	
peace-filled	satisfied	

What kind of child did the psalmist compare the state of his soul to (v. 2)?

A weaned child is a calm and contented child. They aren't squirming around in their mother's arms, looking for milk or the resources she can give; the child is content simply to be in the parent's presence.

Reread verses 1–2. This state of calm and quiet did not come naturally to David. What did he have to actively do to calm and quiet his heart? How can we follow his example?

In these verses, David implied that the state of our souls is directly tied to the gaze of our eyes. If constantly rehearsing unreal conversations or comebacks in our heads; if we continuously worry about things we can do nothing about or imagine situations that might never actually take place; if we constantly picture our lives in a different set of circumstances, with a different spouse, in a different season, in a different job, having made a different set of choices in the past—then we will never know peace. We must train the eyes of our heart to see and think on what is real and true, even if it is someone or something we cannot physically see.

Now, read Philippians 4:5–8. Keep Psalm 131 in mind to help you answer the following questions.

Where did Paul, the author of Philippians, tell us the Lord is (v. 5)?

Since the Lord is near and at hand, what is the posture of our souls supposed to be (v. 6)? (Think back to Psalm 131 for help answering this question.)

What are we supposed to do with things too high, great, hard, and marvelous for us (v. 6)?

As we do those things, what does God give to our hearts (v. 7)?

With the Lord at hand, our eyes fixed on Him, and peace standing guard over our hearts and minds, what kinds of things are we supposed to think on (v. 8)?

Reread Psalm 131:1–2. **Keeping Philippians 4:5–8 in mind, what kinds of things do you think David has to do to keep his gaze steady and actively calm and quiet his heart?**

This, friends, is how we become the Beloved. We train the gaze of our hearts to stay fixed on God as our good Father and to be satisfied with His presence instead of the gifts He can give. We train our eyes to stay fixed on those things that are real, even if they are unseen. We filter everything that happens to us, everything, through the lens of prayer, thanksgiving, trust, and praise.

For some, the gaze or presence of our parents did not bring peace. It made us uncomfortable and set us on edge, because we did not know what kind of mood they were in or consequence they might give.

For some, parents were not consistent in doling out just discipline or consequences. Their gaze meant their wrath, and their wrath meant unjustified anger, harsh words, or abusive physical punishment.

And for others, parents were push-overs. Their no did not mean no, but yes, especially if you asked a thousand times. Deep down, you knew if you kept pushing, at some point they would cave and life could be lived on your terms instead of theirs, even if your terms were not for your greatest good.

Part of our learning to see God and hold His gaze—in good times, hard times, or disciplinary times—is learning to see Him as He really is. His presence always gives His children peace (Psalm 119). Sin is not tolerated in His sight but brought to the light so it can be confessed, cut out, and replaced with righteousness, forgiveness, and peace. His no is always for our good. Always. And His answers do not change. We do not bend His will or His ways through whining, kicking, screaming, tantrum-throwing, or passive-aggressively withdrawing.

Our identity as His beloved children is worked out in our lives as we accept His discipline, consequences, presence, and provision in our lives—in and through every circumstance—as being for our greatest good and His highest praise.

Respond

Father,

For so many years, I have related to You in many of the same ways as I related to my parents. I was afraid and withdrew from You, thinking Your presence was the furthest thing from peace-giving and Your discipline the furthest thing from good. Please forgive me; I repent. Change the eyes of my heart to be fully satisfied with You—just You, not only the good things You give. Train my heart to thank You and see Your goodness and love in and through every circumstance, no matter the answer You give.

DAY 2

Read

Today's Personal Study refers to chapter 16 in the book, "Touch."

Reflect

After looking at the senses of hearing and sight, it's time to turn our attention to touch.

Of all the sensory connections we worked on with Mia Grace, the sense of touch probably amazed me the most. Who knew that all those hours spent in the rocking chair and swaying back and forth with my newborn babies resulted in balance and confidence in their gross motor skills? Who knew that the comfort and touch of my hands would produce such stability in them?

Just as my children flourished under the nurturing touch of my hands, the children of God flourish under the touch of His hands. Working on the sense of touch with God produces three specific things in His children: stability, confidence, and freedom. But the opposite is true as well. When we don't spend time with God allowing His presence and His Word to touch, shape, and ground our lives, the results are instability, insecurity, and fear.

Think for a moment about a parent's touch. The lack of consistent touch, consistent time being held, and consistent time being rocked or swayed in her parents' arms those first seventeen months left a huge deficit in Mia Grace's ability to confidently navigate life. When we adopted her at seventeen months of age, she was barely able to crawl, unable to walk, and could not do simple things like balance well enough to kick a ball or cross a threshold an inch high off the ground.

To understand how we relate to God and receive His touch, we must start by thinking about our relationship to our parents or primary caretakers.

Read through the options below and check which one applies to you.

____ Your parents' touch was consistent, stable, and nurturing. Their touch and availability gave you the confidence and freedom to navigate life from a secure place of love.

____ Your parents' nurturing touch was lacking in your life. Perhaps the lack came from your parents' decision to leave and remain absent, or perhaps the lack came against your parents' will, either through sickness or death.

____ Your parents' nurturing touch was inconsistent in your life. Sometimes it was available to you and sometimes not—you never knew which one it would be.

____ Your parent was present, but the touch you consistency received from them was harsh, punitive, shameful, or inappropriate.

If you experienced lack or inconsistency in a parent's nurturing, stabilizing touch, how do you think that affected your ability to navigate the world around you:

- Physically:
- Emotionally:
- Relationally:

Let's pause for a moment and take a deep breath. Again, those questions could be incredibly difficult for some of you to think through and answer. If that is the case, I am so sorry. Consider taking a break or processing the answers to those questions with a counselor or someone you trust. (Remember to look in the appendix for suggestions on finding someone who can help you from a licensed, Christ-centric perspective.)

If you can continue processing, before we move on to think about the sense of touch in our relationship with God as our Father, I think two things could be helpful or needed here.

One thing we need to do is forgive our parents or anyone who touched us in harmful or inappropriate ways. Again, forgiveness is not a magic wand that makes our hurt or pain disappear; it's a process. But let's be bold, brave, and humble enough to begin that process today.

Before we pray, I want to remind you of something I wrote in the book as well. To admit your parents were at fault or lacking in certain areas of their parenting isn't saying your parents did not love you. Most parents love their children. But parents are unable to love their children perfectly. Only our Father God can do that. For the most part, our parents loved us the best way they knew how. But their faults and lack still left a void or mark on our lives. To honestly admit that mark and hurt is the first step toward healing. The second step toward healing is to forgive. In doing so, you are loving the Lord, yourself, and your parents well.

Consider praying this prayer with me:

Father, I admit honestly and openly I have a lack, mark, or wound in my life from how my parents did or did not touch me securely and appropriately. Their lack of nurturing touch or abundance of punitive or shameful touch harmed me physically, emotionally, and relationally, hindering my ability to relate to others in healthy, confident, and secure ways. I forgive my parents or others for this specific hurt against me: ___________________. I ask that You heal my heart, body, and relationship with You and with others. If restoration is possible in this life, heal and restore the relationship with my parents. Teach me how to honor them and see them through the lens of Your mercy and grace, the same lens through which You see me. Whatever lack I experienced with my parents or primary caretakers, fill to overflowing with Your abundant, steadfast, faithful love and nurturing touch. I no longer want to be defined by my lack but by the abundance of Your faithful presence and my secure relationship with You. Amen.

If you are a parent, the second thing that could be helpful or needed here is to stop and ask for forgiveness from the Lord for any hurt or lack you have caused in your own children and then to receive the forgiveness He freely gives.

Just as our own parents were not perfect, you and I are not perfect parents either. My mom, mother-in-law, and I have spent a great deal of time talking about this. As parents, it's hard to see and admit the hurt we have caused our children. But as the three of us often remind one another, I want to remind you: For this we have Jesus.

If you and I were perfect parents, where would the need be in our children's lives for the Lord? The very lack in my mom, mother-in-law, and me caused by our parents or other people we love has been the very thing that has drawn us the closest to Christ. We pray the same is true for our own children.

This isn't an excuse or an attempt to brush off or disregard the hurt we cause in our children's lives, but it is truth that offers us hope—God uses all things for good in our children's lives, even the hurt we ourselves caused. It's a humbling but true realization. Our prayer for our children isn't that we would be perfect parents, but that in our lack, our children would find Christ and find Him to be enough.

In my own process of moving toward healing and earned secure attachment, I have faced many hard truths about myself as a parent. Several times, I have had to ask forgiveness from the Lord and from my daughters, but I have found that there is great healing in the process of repair and restoration. When I am humble enough to repent to my children and admit my lack, great healing and restoration flows, not only in my own life but in their lives as well. After times of honesty and repentance, our relationship emerges stronger than it ever was before. If you are a parent, please do not despair. Healing and freedom are found in asking and receiving forgiveness for the sins we have committed as parents as much as it is in forgiving our own parents.

Consider praying this prayer along with me:

Father, it is so painful and humbling to see honestly and admit openly the ways I have hurt my children. I am an imperfect parent; You are the only perfect Father. Please forgive me for my sin of __________________ toward my children. Whatever hurt I have caused in them, please heal and restore with Your perfect love. If restoration is possible in this lifetime, please open the door for me to ask for forgiveness from my child. Prepare and soften their hearts to hear what I have to say, and restore and redeem our relationship Your time and Your way. Please lift any shame I carry from the hurt I have knowingly or unknowingly caused in my children. Change the way I interact with and relate to my children as I understand and receive more of the knowledge of Your steadfast, unending love.

I know this might have been a tough day for many of you, so with that in mind, let's close with a word of comfort, healing, and hope, straight from our Father's heart.

Turn to Psalm 32 and read slowly through verses 1–7.

Who is the blessed person?

What happens when you keep silent about your sin, either sin you have committed or sin committed against you?

What did David need to do to receive forgiveness?

What else does the repentant person receive? What does God become?

When we admit the lack in our own lives and the hurt we have caused in others, God becomes enough. He becomes our hiding place, and His touch fills, stabilizes, heals, protects, preserves, and surrounds us, all because we have chosen to call upon Him. Today, may God's presence through His Word continue to comfort your heart.

Respond

Father,
Confessing sin, extending forgiveness, and asking for forgiveness is never comfortable or easy, but it is the only place where true healing is found. Please continue this good work of restoration in me as I lean into You as my hiding place, trust Your stabilizing touch, and hear Your songs of deliverance. Thank You for being the perfect Father and for always being enough.

Continuing the Calm

Your sense of touch is a powerful one. If touch has been used against you, you may have developed a very real disconnection with your body. This is a very normal coping mechanism people subconsciously develop to protect themselves during prolonged periods of abuse. Once the danger has passed, this disconnection lingers. If you think this may be true about yourself, you might try focusing on an area of your body of which you are afraid. There may be residual pain. There may be lack of feeling. The truth is that your body and mind are still trying to protect you from danger that has passed. The good news is restoration of that connection can occur. Here are some good options for beginning the process of reconnecting:

- You might begin by spending focused time petting a dog or other pet and noticing your safety as you do. Spend time really noticing your connection via touch and the positive feelings associated with this.
- A next level step might be to watch simple stretching videos on YouTube and follow along. As you do, notice the sensations in the different areas that are being stretched. Notice that you are safe and that your body is under your own control.
- Many people find that going to restorative yoga or Pilates is a safe and beneficial place to reconnect with their bodies. While any "meditative" time in yoga should certainly be directed to prayer and engaging with our heavenly Father, I also encourage you to notice the safety you now experience in your body.
- Whatever option you choose to re-engage with your body, don't miss God in the middle of it. Praying and thanking Him for each stretch, touch, or ability to feel throughout the process keeps Him at the center.

God is the restorer of all things and wants all truth to be brought to light. When He calls us to love Him with all our heart, mind, body, and soul, He means all of it. This means He cares about restoration in all areas of our lives, our bodies included. The amazing thing is that restoration of one part of your life is directly connected to all the others. As you seek God and find that He is your hiding place, He will give you the strength to overcome fear and face these physical obstacles that might seem impossible. He is your Good Shepherd who tenderly cares for you and is not afraid of your physical pain. Rather, He sees it and knows hope and healing are found in Him alone.

DAY 3

Read

Today's Personal Study refers to chapter 16 in the book, "Touch."

Reflect

After looking at the ways our parents' or primary caretakers' touch affected us, let's turn our attention to God. Remember that the touch of God's hands produces three specific things in His children: stability, confidence, and freedom. Without His consistent touch, we are prone to instability, insecurity, and fear.

Think for a moment about your relationship with God. If you did not receive the nurturing, stabilizing touch you needed from your earthly parents, how do you see this affecting your relationship with God? Do you struggle to feel secure, confident, and free in relationship with Him and in navigating the world around you? If so, how does that play out on a regular basis?

Like Mia Grace as a toddler with Jason and me, feeling secure in my heavenly Father's touch was something I really had to work on as an adult. As His children, we were meant to be the most confident, secure, stable, and free people on the planet. But so often, we are just as unstable and insecure as everyone else.

For help in understanding the answer to that question, let's quickly review Psalm 40:1–2.

The first two verses of Psalm 40 imply that if our feet are standing on anything other than the rock, it's just a matter of time before we will sink in a pit of destruction or miry bog. But who or what is this rock?

Now, read Psalm 118:22–23.

Fill in the blanks below from verse 22 and then answer the questions that follow:

The __________________ that the builders rejected has become the __________________.

Who do you think the stone referred to in this verse?

What has this "rejected stone" become?

Any time we see the word "stone" or "rock" in Scripture, the reference is often to Christ Himself. He is the rock or stone God places our feet on so that our steps can become secure. And the more time we spend with Him, the more stable our footing becomes.

Think for a moment: when you are in a moment of feeling insecure, unstable, or overwhelmed, what people or things are you often tempted to secure yourself on apart from Christ? Circle any that apply.

Friends	Accomplishments	Significant other
Wealth	Parents	Children's accomplishments
Education	Spouse	Comforts or standard of living
Job	Extended family	Connections to influential people
House/Neighborhood	Children	

Now, for any of the items you circled, list specifics (names of friends or groups of friends, comforts you can't do without, etc.).

Now list the ways you most often or naturally turn to in order to steady or secure yourself (texting or calling a person or specific group of people to gossip, slander, or tear someone down; purchasing something online or in a store; eating, drinking alcohol, watching a show, looking at pornography, etc.).

When God initially rescues us in that moment of salvation when we place our trust in Christ, our lives immediately become secure. We are rescued from the ultimate pit of death and destruction, and we are placed in an immovable, secure place of eternal relationship with Jesus Christ. But part of the process of growing in our relationship with Christ is allowing Him to move our feet from standing on any other person or thing that brings us security and placing our trust in Him alone. While that process is often painful, it is ultimately good.

If you are anything like me, you are unable to move your feet from wallowing in an unstable place or group of people to standing on the secure rock of Christ. You are completely incapable of cutting ties that need to be cut, walking away from unhealthy relationships or circumstances that keep you bound, or giving up wealth or positions or jobs or status that makes you feel important, giving you a false illusion of stability.

But God has a unique way of delivering us from all our insecurities and instabilities. He often does it through pain and suffering. He often uses the feel of sinking ground—abandonment, betrayal, loss, sickness, suffering, bankruptcy, global pandemics, financial hardship, and relational difficulties—to help us recognize, understand, and know just how stable He alone is.

In her book *Keep a Quiet Heart*, Elisabeth Elliot says, "[God] is not all we would ask for (if we were honest), but it is precisely when we do not have what we would ask for, and *only then,* that we can clearly perceive His all-sufficiency. It is when the sea is moonless that the Lord has become my Light."[25]

I would add: It is when all other ground is sinking that God becomes my rock. And it is in those moments when we are literally sinking that He rescues us. He does what we cannot do for ourselves—He moves our feet to stable ground.

Let's pause for a moment. In 2020–2021, God used a global pandemic to show all of us just how unstable everything else in our world is except for Him.

What specific things in the past several years can you look back on and identify as sinking ground—ground that before the pandemic, or a specific season of loss in your life, you were certain was stable and solid but now realize was a miry bog?

How did God use a very shaky, unstable season to help transfer your trust, confidence, and security to Him?

Is there anything you are still holding onto, still using to steady and secure yourself, when you know your confidence should be in God alone? If so, what is that person or thing?

Like David, take a moment to stop, cry out, and ask God to deliver you and move your feet to stable ground.

Father, so often, I am tempted to place my trust, confidence, and security in ____________________ instead of in You. Please forgive me. I know I cannot deliver myself; only You can rescue me. Please do what I cannot do for myself in the days and weeks ahead and set my feet upon the rock of Christ, the only steady, unshakeable ground.

Let's close today by reading 1 Peter 2:4–5, 9.

As we come to Christ, our living stone, rejected by people but precious in the sight of God, what are we being built into (v. 5)?

What kind of identity do we have as living stones (v. 9)?

What is our purpose?

The process of learning to secure ourselves and be confident in the rock of Christ alone can be difficult, lonely, and painful. God often takes away people or things near and dear to our hearts and allows lack in tender places to build us into a people whose foundation is Him and Him alone. He loves us too much to do anything else. C.S. Lewis says it this way,

> Imagine yourself as a living house. God comes in to rebuild that house. At first, perhaps, you can understand what He is doing. He is getting the drains right and stopping the leaks in the roof and so on: you knew that those jobs

> needed doing and so you are not surprised. But presently he starts knocking the house about in a way that hurts abominably and does not seem to make sense. What on earth is He up to? The explanation is that He is building quite a different house from the one you thought of—throwing out a new wing here, putting on an extra floor there, running up towers, making courtyards. You thought you were going to be made into a decent little cottage: but He is building a palace. He intends to come and live in it Himself.[26]

When the going gets tough and you are in a painful season of learning to secure yourself in the hands of God, remember what you are being built into. Remember what your identity really is and the purpose for which you have been created. You are a living stone, chosen and precious to God, who is building you and all those who love the Lord Jesus Christ into a place where He Himself loves to dwell.

Respond

Father,
Whatever void or instability exists in my life from lack or inconsistency of a parent's touch, Your hands are more than enough to fill. Thank You that the more time I spend with You, the more secure my steps become. In Your faithfulness, plant my feet on the rock of Christ, lifting me out of the miry bog of standing on anyone or anything else but You. Thank You for promising to make my steps secure.

DAY 4

Read

Today's Personal Study refers to chapter 16 in the book, "Touch."

Reflect

When Jason and I worked with Mia Grace on securing her steps, teaching her to walk, helping her to cross thresholds in a single bound, it wasn't rocket science that helped her steps become more secure—it was trust and time. She had to learn to trust that we were good parents and that holding onto our hands and spending time in our arms was safe. She also had to be willing to come out of the small, confined spaces where she liked to play and learn to spend time walking, swinging on swings, riding on tricycles, and enjoying the wide, open spaces our hands provided to be free.

The same is true with you and me. Stability, security, confidence, and freedom come the more time we spend letting go of other people and things we use to stabilize ourselves and holding onto our Father's hands.

Read Psalm 15:1–5.

Who "sojourns" in God's tent, and dwells, abides, remains, and settles in God's holy hill or house? I can count at least eleven characteristics of this person. List at least five of them that stand out to you.

For us to do any of these things or to become the kind of person Psalm 15 describes requires one thing: time. We need time in God's presence, time in God's house, and time in God's Word. Left on our own, we can never speak the truth in our heart, keep from slandering with our tongue, refuse to take up an offense against a friend, or do what is right. It's impossible—unless we spend time with our heavenly Father, letting His touch stabilize our lives and secure our steps.

When we commit to time in God's presence, God's house, and God's Word, what kind of person do we become (v. 5)?

I remember the first time I read, studied, and really prayed through this psalm. I got to the end of verse 5 and wept. That was the kind of person I wanted to be—a person who was never moved. Never unstable. Never insecure. Never leaning on another person or thing for my balance or security. My insecurity through the years had brought me so much pain. Slowly but surely, God has answered that prayer. The more time I spend in my Father's house, looking in my Father's eyes, listening to and obeying my Father's voice, surrendering to my Father's touch, holding onto my Father's hands—the more confident, secure, immoveable, and free I have become. Not because I am so strong, but because the rock underneath my feet is so secure.

We are often tempted to think the opposite. We are tempted to think that the more time we spend being dependent, leaning on our Father's hands, stabilizing ourselves in His presence—the more restricted or confined our lives become. But nothing could be further from the truth.

Read Psalm 119:30–32.

In the space below, I have written the first part of each phrase from these verses. Fill in the second part. I have done the first one for you:

- I have chosen: <u>the way of faithfulness</u>
- I set: ______________________________
- I cling: ______________________________
- I will run: ______________________________

Answer me honestly here—does this sound like a boring or exciting way to live? Constricting or freeing? Delightful or demanding? Explain.

I hear you; I hear you. Quite frankly, it sounds awful, boring, dry, dull, and restricting.

But look at the very last part of verse 32. What happened to the psalmist's heart as he chose the way of obedience to God's commands?

Another translation of Scripture says it this way: "I shall run the way of Your commandments, for You will enlarge my heart" (NASB). Choosing to obey God's commands, run the path of His righteous rules, and cling to His testimonies isn't restrictive—it's the only way that leads to true freedom.

When we are slaves to securing ourselves on other people or things besides God, like Mia Grace, we live in cramped, confined, and narrow spaces. But when we allow God's Word to examine us instead of us examining it; when we say, "I will obey no matter what Your Word tells me to do"; when we trust the path God leads us down—narrow as it might seem—it leads to large, open spaces, and our hearts, perhaps for the very first time, become free. We are free to obey, free to trust, free to follow, free to secure our lives on the only One who has the power and ability to remain steadfast and trustworthy come what may.

Like the psalmist, if you want to live a life that is free with a big heart, hold onto God's hands. Trust God's path. Spend time in God's Word. Enjoy God's presence as God's child, and confidence, security, stability, freedom, and joy will come.

Respond

Father,

For so much of my life, freedom has meant doing what I what when I want to do it. But if I am honest, that has only led to insecurity, instability, brokenness, and fear. Help me to trust You enough to spend time in Your presence, allowing Your Word to examine me and Your hands to steady me, setting my heart free.

DAY 5

Read

Today's Personal Study refers to chapter 17 in the book, "Taste."

Reflect

Today and the first two days of next week, I want to spend time digging into our sense of taste to understand how it relates to secure attachment to our heavenly Father.

I lived for a long time with a taste of shame, bitterness, and envy in my mouth. I started to think there was no possibility for change. But as the Lord began to restore Mia Grace's sense of taste, He began to restore mine as well. Instead of being met with the punishment I thought I deserved or the disappointment from God I thought I earned, I was met with a meal of grace. I can't even type the word without tearing up. I'm as amazed today as I was several years ago when God sat me down and started to intentionally make me look at the meal He truly offered at His table—not the meal I had imagined or thought I had to choke down for so many years.

This meal of grace is what I want you to taste as well. It doesn't matter how much you've messed up, how great your plans for your life were and how flawed you've become, or how greatly you've failed. Our Father loves to fill our plates with mercy and our cups with grace.

Read slowly through all six verses of Psalm 23. We prayed through this psalm at the beginning of Week 4, but today, I want to think about it in the context of the table God has prepared for you.

For many years, I thought this psalm was about death and reserved for funerals and gravesites. What I have come to learn is that this psalm is about life—the restored life God offers us in the here and now and in the life to come.

In your Bible, highlight every occurrence of me, my, or I in this passage.

Have you ever thought about the fact that the Lord is your shepherd? Yours. All the meals He serves you, cups He offers you, pastures where He takes you, paths where He leads you are personal to you. It's not you and a thousand other sheep; it's you. When I think of our Good Shepherd through this lens and the relationship I have with Him in this way, I am stunned by the abundance of personalized grace rather than the lack of it.

In his book *The Good Shepherd*, Kenneth Bailey says, "No sheep is ever taken out to pasture alone. The cost of the labor involved would be prohibitive. A flock is thereby always assumed. But in this famous psalm, the focus is on the individual. David is describing his own spiritual journey."[27]

I want you to know something: the table God has set for you and for me as our Good Shepherd is a table we can trust. It is not set for you plus your thousand closest friends. It is set for you, personally prepared for your unique set of trials, your unique series of valleys, your unique string of troubles with enemies. When we have this kind of perspective, the meals God has prepared for us become easier to swallow. Instead of choking things down in bitterness, we can learn to swallow in trust and thankfulness, knowing they have been personally and individually prepared for our good.

Before we begin to delve into the topic of grace, I want you to think about something for a moment: if you have a hard time accepting the circumstances or meal set before you by the Lord with a grateful heart, what was the table in your house like growing up?

Did your family sit around the table together regularly for meals? If not, why not?

Was the table in your home a place where you felt heard, seen, and valued by your family members? If not, what was the atmosphere around the table like?

Think about your relationship to food in your home growing up. Was there always enough to eat, or did you often go hungry?

If your mom or dad made nourishing, healthy meals, did they ask you to eat what was set in front of you, or did they regularly allow you to eat something else if you did not like what was served? Explain.

Now step back for a moment and think about how your experiences with food and around the table in your childhood home affect your relationship with God as your parent and primary caretaker now.

If your family did not regularly sit down together for meals, is the metaphor of the table of the Lord a difficult one for you to picture or envision? Explain.

If the table in your home was not a place where you felt heard, seen, and valued, is it difficult for you to feel like you possess a special or significant place at God's table? Why or why not?

If the atmosphere around your table growing up was tense, chaotic, or a place where you often felt corrected or ashamed, do you often envision the Lord as being disappointed in you, angry, or irritated? Explain.

If there was not enough food in your home growing up, or if the amount of food you ate was closely watched or regulated, do you struggle with trusting God will provide for your daily needs? Do you struggle with the need to tightly control events in your daily life and wrestle with anxiety or fear? Explain.

Finally, if you often rejected the nourishing food set in front of you, do you struggle with contentment and gratitude over the circumstances God allows in your life in the here and now? Why do you think that is?

My table in my childhood home was one of the safest places to be. Not only was my mom a wonderful cook, but she loved to create beautiful table centerpieces and an atmosphere around the table where everyone felt heard, included, valued, and loved. Dinner times were non-negotiable. It didn't matter how much homework we had left to do. My brothers and I all stopped whatever we were doing to eat, fellowship, and have a family devotional around the table. If we did not like the food that was served, it didn't matter. We were expected to take at least three bites and sit and wait for everyone else to finish.

While those memories of mealtimes might sound restrictive, they were actually the best part of my day. I never laughed as hard or shared as much as I did around the table. My mom and dad did a wonderful job of making it a safe and beautiful place to be. But for whatever reason, that sense of grace, laughter, and joy I encountered around my parents' table didn't translate for me to God's table.

I walked around constantly feeling like God was disappointed with me. I believed I was continually failing God's Plan A for my life, and He was having to serve me Plan B or even Plan C. Because of that, I envied people around me who looked like they were getting to enjoy Plan A. I struggled with bitterness, always wondering if I would ever get my life together enough to have the meal I wanted off the menu as well.

It took really meditating on and praying through one specific Scripture for the lie I believed to surface and the truth to take its place.

Reread Psalm 23:5.

Where did God prepare a table for you and for me?

What enemies do you think the psalmist was referring to—literal, physical enemies, emotional or spiritual enemies, or both? Explain.

Now, read Galatians 5:17–21.

What enemy is against the desires of God's Holy Spirit in you (v. 17)?

Which of the enemies, or works of the flesh, do you regularly struggle with (vv. 19–21)? Circle any that apply.

Sexual immorality	Strife	Envy
Impurity	Jealousy	Drunkenness
Sensuality	Fits of anger	Orgies
Idolatry	Rivalries	Other things like these that come to mind:
Sorcery	Dissensions	
Enmity	Divisions	____________________

If you circled several of them, don't worry—you're in good company. I'm right there with you. But let me ask you a question. Where do those enemies come from?

Here was the turning point for me for healing and restoration in my sense of taste with the Lord: the enemies He wanted and waited so patiently to deliver me from were enemies of my very own making. They came from desires inside of me, not from somewhere or someone else.

But where I always thought God looked at me with a tight-lipped, disappointed scowl on His face when saw my life and the enemies of my own making, Psalm 23:5 caught me by surprise.

Read it one more time, and then write it out in your own words.

When God sees you and me—His sheep—caught, trapped, overwhelmed and overcome by enemies, full of anger and shame, arms crossed, bitter, envious, with a headache from too much to drink or a weighty conscience from behaving in an immoral way, He doesn't scowl at us or walk away from us. He prepares a table for us.

Friends, if this doesn't move you, I don't know what will. God prepares a table for us in the presence of our enemies, even enemies of our own making. Preparing a table means God prepares for you a place where you are nurtured, seen, valued, and heard; a place where the meal set in front of you is prepared specifically for your trials, your valleys, your hurts, your joys, your triumphs, and your disappointments; a place where you are met with grace and goodness, goodness that you did not earn and certainly do not deserve.

Read Galatians 5:22–23.

What is the meal the Spirit of God serves you?

Read Galatians 5:24–26.

How do we learn to eat this meal of grace?

Eating grace requires us to receive grace. Like we have talked about before, it means we must admit we are very real sinners, repent of our sin, and then purposefully push aside the anger, bitterness, unforgiveness, and envy we are so used to choking down and learn to eat the meal set before us at our Father's table.

We must learn to see God as He really is—full of mercy and good fruit, ever ready to welcome repentant sinners home, pulling out their place at the table—instead of the disappointed, far-off, irritated, arms-crossed, passive, or absent parent we have imagined Him to be.

The best way to know if you are seated at God's table, eating the meal of mercy and grace He has prepared for you is this: are you able to offer that same meal to others around you, especially your enemies?

If you cannot: if you hold onto unforgiveness with a tight and determined grip; if you have continual conversations telling others off in your head; if you easily take offense against other people and are quick to build walls—chances are, you are not sitting down at your Father's table.

You cannot offer to others what you have not first received for yourself. I know because this is how I lived for several years. I couldn't extend grace because I wasn't eating grace. I couldn't extend mercy because I was rejecting mercy, demanding perfection for myself and others around me.

If that is you, stop. Get down on your knees; pray and ask God to teach you how to eat the meal at His table, how to see Him for who He really is, how to see yourself for who you really are, how to repent, and how to receive grace—the grace that is ever and always Plan A for your life.

From this day on, may you and I determine to eat the meal set before us at the table of the God who loves us and gave Himself for us so we could become His children.

Respond

Father,

Forgive me for doubting the goodness of Your table; forgive me for questioning Your faithful love; forgive me for comparing, even subconsciously, my childhood table to the table in Your house; forgive me for bowing to and serving a false image of You, an image that has been entirely of my own making. Help me to see You as You really are—my Good Shepherd who lays down His life for His sheep (John 10:11). Help me remember Your meal is set in the presence of my enemies, even enemies of my own making. As I eat the goodness and mercy You have set before me, may it nourish my heart in such a way that I can offer it to others. Thank You for giving me a place at Your table.

WEEK 7

Rebuilding the Senses, Part III

Abe & Sarah

↓

Isaac & Rebekah

↓

Jacob / Leah & Rachel
+ 2 servants

↓

4 women, 12 kids
that become 12 tribes
of Israel.

- Jacob struggles his whole life w/ wanting to be first.
- Jacob gets everything he wants, but only thru deceitful means.

VIEWER GUIDE: WEEK 7

- Jacob was the 1st in scripture to refer to God as his shepherd.

A LIFE RESTORED

Jacob

GENESIS 32 :3-12

Deliver: to recover & rescue

- We are restored as we are delivered from fear.
  - God first delivers or rescues Jacob from himself.
  - Like Jacob, all of us must be delivered from ourselves and from our fear:

    The fear of never measuring up

    The fear of being less than (shift our definition of success)

    The fear of being left out — our place at the table is secure.

    The fear of having to dress up and pretend to be someone other than ourselves to receive a blessing

· fear keeps us on the run

° we are people-pleasers rather than God-pleasers

· these things shrink our souls.

- We are restored as we are delivered to fear.
  - We must be delivered to a fear of God.
  - Fear of God is a great, big, glorious wide fear that opens our eyes, expands our vision, and enlarges and restores our souls.

- this wresting is a wounding.
- the pathway to our greatest blessing is straight thru our fear.

- We are restored as we remember who we are.

- We are restored as we receive true blessing.

  - The blessing of God's face and God's name means He has given us revelation of who He is along with His promise to be envoked and involved in our lives.

Video Sessions available at susannahbaker.com/biblestudies.

- Jacob didn't get a blessing until he said his name + remembers who he is.
- Jacob: his name meant "to grasp + deceive."
  - God changes his name to Israel: an entire group who persevere + persist w/ God
- Peniel (to turn on to face God)
- Israel: a name he didn't earn. He can't lose it!
- We don't have to earn a seat @ the table. We already have it! We can't lose it!
- His limp / wound is what will help him remember to turn to God.
- Num 6:24-27
- God's face on us is the true blessing we ~~receive~~ receive from God! (not what He gives us → but His very presence)

PERSONAL STUDY

Before beginning this week's study, please review chapter 17 and read chapters 18–19 of the book.

DAY 1

Read

Today's Personal Study refers to chapter 17, "Taste."

Reflect

It's hard to believe we are on our last week of Personal Study. The last six weeks have not been easy—heart work never is. But my prayer is that you not only begin to see fruitfulness and breakthrough in patterns in your life you thought would never change but that you would see breakthrough in relationships with your spouse, children, extended family, coworkers, and friends as well. As the prophet Isaiah wrote, "For thus said the Lord GOD, the Holy One of Israel, 'In [repentance] and rest you shall be saved; in quietness and trust shall be your strength'" (Isaiah 30:15). Repentance does not feel like safety and salvation, but it is. Quietness and trust do not feel like strength, but nothing is stronger than total trust in the Lord. The work you have done rebuilding through repentance, honesty, restoration, and reliance on the Lord will bear good fruit in you and in generations to come.

We'll spend today and tomorrow thinking through two more restorative aspects of God's table and our taste, and then we will turn to our final sense, scent.

When we think about restoring our taste, like Mia Grace, one of the biggest challenges we must overcome is learning to let go of our desire for control and our fear to trust our parents enough to swallow the meal they set before us. This process of letting go of the desire for control and fear took years for Mia Grace, so this is not something we accomplish overnight—slowly but surely, we can begin to move our feet in the right direction.

We primarily learn to swallow the meal that is placed before by trusting the hand that feeds us. That is easy enough for us to do when the food in front of us is a fun vacation, a job well done, or a satisfying marriage or attentive spouse. But what if the food God allows looks bitter at first glance? What if we wanted dessert and get Brussels sprouts instead?

Read Hebrews 12:7–11.

Circle the word "discipline" in verse 7. Why does God allow discipline in our lives?

Just as our discipline in what we eat reveals our priorities for our health, so our spiritual discipline reveals our priorities in life. If you only desire the "chocolate cake" of life and balk at anything unpleasant, painful, difficult, or hard, what does this say about your relationship with God? (Hint: Take a look at verse 8.)

Now, focus on verse 10 for a minute. Why does God discipline us and allow difficult or hard circumstances in our lives?

No matter how unpleasant discipline tastes at the time, what kind of fruit, or food, does it produce in our lives (v. 11)?

Here is where our mindset about the meal placed before us needs to change: God allows unpleasant tastes for our good. You and I cannot grow into the healthy, strong, joyful, loving, peaceful, confident children He created us to be by eating only the sweet tasting things of life. We know that in our heads, but it is so hard to accept, live out, and respond to graciously in our hearts.

On the days when it just seems too hard to choke down the unpleasant tasting meal, where do you think we can draw our encouragement?

Read Hebrews 12:3.
How would you change your answer to the previous question?

Friends, on our hardest days, we must do what the writer of Hebrews commands us to do: consider Jesus. Any bitter portion we must eat pales in comparison to the cup He drank and the meal He ate on our behalf.

Now, read Hebrews 4:15–16.
When our enemy, sin, tempts us to stumble and fall—either sin committed against us or sin of our own making—when we draw near to Jesus, what do we find and receive every single time?

What we are told in these verses lines up exactly with what David wrote in Psalm 23:5 one thousand years before: God has prepared a table for us in the presence of our enemies. When we are in seasons of trial and tempted to become bitter, envious, divisive, angry, or contentious—we must consider Jesus, sit down at His table, receive mercy, and find grace in your time of need.

Read Psalm 34:8–10.

As we learn to do this, what can we confidently say along with the psalmist?

When we look at Jesus, we can swallow the food. When we look at Jesus, we can trust the hand that feeds us. When we look at Jesus, we know "He who did not spare his own Son but gave him up for us all" will "with him graciously give us all things" (Romans 8:32).

Mia Grace did not eventually start to swallow her food, conquer her fear, and let go of her need to tightly control every bite that went into her mouth because my cooking greatly improved. She started to swallow because she knew the person who fed her loved her, spent time with her, came to get her when she cried and expressed need, and kept coming day after day, night after night, and meal after meal. If I, as a very imperfect parent, can instill that kind of trust in my daughter, what can the presence and provision of Your heavenly Father instill in you?

What has God set before you that you might be tempted to push away, not wanting to eat?

What lie or lies do you believe about the goodness and character of God every time you look at that meal or circumstance?

Take a moment to think about your circumstance, and then turn your eyes upon Jesus. Consider Him. As you do so, can you take the bite and swallow? Can you trust Him and know that even if the circumstance is not good, He will bring good from it? Can you trust Him and know that the discipline and hardship He allows is for your good and is proof that you are His beloved child, His legitimate daughter?

Take a moment to consider Jesus with the eyes of your heart, and then write out your response to Him.

My friend, pull up a chair, pick up a fork, take a bite, and swallow. The peaceful fruit of righteousness is waiting for all those who trust the Lord enough to eat His meal.

Respond

Father,
"All shall work together for good; everything is needful that [You] send; nothing can be needful that [You] withhold."[28] In and through every difficult circumstance and unpleasant meal, help me to consider Jesus. "If [I] seem to get no good by attempting to draw near Him [I] may be sure [I] shall get none by keeping away from Him."[29] Turn the eyes of my heart upon Him, enabling me to trust the hand that feeds me, loves me, and will use all things for my good.

DAY 2

Read

Today's Personal Study refers to chapter 17 in the book, "Taste."

Reflect

While an important aspect of rebuilding our taste is learning to trust the goodness of the Lord even when the meal set before us is bitter or difficult to eat, another important aspect of rebuilding our taste is trusting the size of the daily portion in front of us is enough.

Remember, when Jesus taught His disciples to pray, He taught them to ask for one very specific thing. Review Matthew 6:9–13, and then write out verse 11.

Circle the word "daily."

How much do you think a "daily" portion of bread would be? How big would your plate need to be to hold it? Would you need a backpack or pickup truck to haul it off? Would you need to rent a van to cart it all away? Heavens no! You would a plate—maybe two if you were a growing teenager.

The Greek church father, Chrysostom, explained that the phrase "daily bread" means "that . . . which is needed for our daily support of life. It is that bread which is needful to the *ousia*, substance, of our being, that will sustain us."[30] We are to ask only for that which we can carry in our own two hands—daily bread. Daily provision. Frankly, you and I can't handle carrying around anything more than that. We are too frail and too weak to handle anything more than today's needs.

Yet we are hoarders. We try to stuff our plates, backpacks, purses, and sacks with enough bread for the next ten years. Or at least enough until our kids have all safely made it through high school. But what happens to the bread we try to take, the worries we try to borrow, the anxieties we insist on carrying that have absolutely nothing to do with today?

God gave us an incredible visual in Exodus 16 of exactly what happens when we try to take more than enough for one day. When God delivered His people from slavery in Egypt and took them by way of the wilderness to their new home, the promised land, the people had one problem: they needed to eat. Every day.

This may not sound like a big deal, unless you consider that there were an estimated two million Israelites trekking across the desert who all needed to eat every day. Not only is that a lot of mouths to feed, but the wilderness they were in did not offer much in the way of nourishment.

Read Exodus 16:1–3.

Where did the Israelites arrive after setting out from Elim?

How did the Israelites respond to being in the wilderness and needing food to eat?

Let's pause for a second. You have to wonder what God thought about all of this. He'd just delivered two million people from slavery and the tyranny of Pharaoh's hand with miracle after miracle, an appearance of the angel of death, and a dramatic parting of the Red Sea. And yet, these very same people were wondering if He was good enough or powerful enough to give them a simple thing like bread, wishing they had died in Egypt as slaves sitting by pots of meat. Thankfully, God isn't like us, because, I think I would have decided right then and there to leave those ungrateful people to their own demise in the desert. Thank goodness none of that is up to us. Ever.

Now, read Exodus 16:4–5.

What was God's answer to His people's grumbling and hunger pains?

Except for the sixth day, in preparation for the Sabbath, how much bread from heaven were the Israelites to gather every day?

God's answer to His people's grumbling was essentially this: "Every day, I'll give you exactly what you need for that day—not a day more, not a day less. And the proof that You love Me and trust Me to continue to provide for you is that you gather only enough for the day."

Continue reading in Exodus 16:14–21.

What happened if the people left some of the manna until the next morning? What was Moses's response to this?

Look back at verse 18. What happened to those who gathered "an omer," the measurement that represented a portion for one day?

When Jesus taught His disciples to ask the Lord for "daily bread," approximately 1500 years had passed since the Exodus and the Israelites' wandering in the wilderness. But while cultures, world powers, and rulers had changed, the human heart had not. Jesus knew His people could only handle carrying enough bread for the day. Holding onto anything more than that would rot and turn to worms in the form of worry, anxiety, tension, stress, and fear.

Two thousand years after Christ's death, resurrection, and ascension, the human heart still has not changed. All we can handle carrying around is enough bread for the day. All our hearts can hold are today's burdens, today's issues, today's needs, and today's requests. To attempt to gather anymore manna or stuff our cheeks with anymore bread than today's portion is arrogance at best and downright rebellion to God's law at worst.

Take a look at Matthew 6:31–34.

Jesus taught the rules of the table to a new generation of Israelites. These same rules still apply to us today.

List the things Jesus said not to be anxious about.

What are we to spend our time gathering or seeking? As we do so, what will then be added or given to us?

When Christ came and walked on this earth, the rules of the table slightly changed. Instead of spending our day gathering physical bread, what kind of bread are we to gather? (Before giving your answer, read John 6:35 too.)

Friends, hear me on this: focusing on worry, gathering up anxiety, putting all our energy on storing up provision for days, weeks, and years in advance profits nothing in the kingdom of God. In fact, as we have discussed, our worry turns to rot and anxiety to internal worms.

But when we focus on our Father, trusting Him for our daily bread, spending our time and energy on seeking first His kingdom, His rule and reign, His right ways of relating to Jesus and the people around us—all that we need, everything else that we seek, will be given.

Oh, that we would only believe this! How different our lives would look from the people who do not know God around us.

Are you trying to hold onto more than what you need for today? If so, what are you trying to hold on to?

Now think for a moment: Why are you trying to hold on to more than what you need for today? What lie do you believe about the character, power, or provision of God?

Sit quietly for a minute and ask the Lord to show you what kind of internal fruit your lack of trust in His daily provision is producing in you—worry, stress, tension, teeth-grinding, jaw-clenching, heart-racing, anger, or fear. Describe what He brings to mind.

What lie you believe or behavior do you need repent for right now?

How might you replace the lie and affirm the truth about God, His Word, and His ways?

Name the specific need for today or the future do you need to surrender into God's hands.

As we close today, remember this: the provision of Christ in you and the hope of His glory, goodness, redemption, and restoration is enough for every need, every day, at every table. May you trust Him enough to gather and store only what you need for today, leaving tomorrow's worries and cares in His hands.

Respond

Father,
Learning to live by the rules of Your table is so counter-intuitive, counter-cultural, and so hard. Please forgive me for not trusting You enough to provide for my daily needs. Open my hands and help me release my grip on worry, fear, and control so I can seek the things that matter: Your kingdom, Your rule and reign, and right relationship with You and others. Remind me every day to ask for and be satisfied with the daily bread that comes straight from Your hand.

Continuing the Calm

Philippians 4:6–7 teaches us, "do not be anxious about anything, but in everything by prayer and supplication with thanksgiving let your requests be made known to God. And the peace of God, which surpasses all understanding, will guard your hearts and your minds in Christ Jesus." Modern psychology has found the same thing to be true (although it tends to exclude the prayer aspect): thanksgiving is the most powerful tool against anxiety and depression.

There are certainly issues with the worldly take on this wisdom but look at it from a different angle. If thanksgiving is that powerful a combatant in our own human strength, how much more is its value when it is joined through prayer with the Creator of the universe?

When it seems impossible to focus on just your daily bread and the needs for today, while the worry of tomorrow seems insurmountable, I encourage you to remember Philippians 4:6–7. Within it is a step-by-step instruction list. You can even write it out as follows (and if you have a current worry, I encourage you to do so now).

Don't be anxious. Stop. Let's put that worry on the shelf for a moment and redirect our focus.

By prayer and supplication . . . let your requests be known to God. What are your prayers? What are your needs? What are you worrying about and need help from your heavenly Father to overcome? Write this out here and pray it out loud.

. . . with thanksgiving. What today, right now, in the middle of your circumstances, can you be thankful for? That list goes here. Small or large, include anything you can think of.

Let your heart bring your specific thanks to the Lord and find your rest in Him. Notice that He has given you much to be thankful for, and He will not leave you alone in your circumstances. Your worry is safe in His hands. This is where His peace that transcends all understanding will guard your heart and mind in Christ Jesus.

DAY 3

Read

Today's Personal Study refers to chapter 18 in the book, "Scent."

Reflect

Today and tomorrow we turn our attention to the last of our senses: scent. While scent might be the one the most difficult to understand and relate to our secure attachment to our heavenly Father, it plays an important role in learning how to live like our Father's children.

There are certain smells that are universally recognized as being repugnant—smells like rotten food, human waste, and death. That is because each of those smells tells us danger or harm is close by and we need to stay away or keep our distance, for our own safety and protection.

With that in mind, look at Ephesians 2:1–5 below. We have looked at this passage before, but today I want us to look at it through the lens of restored and renewed scent.

> And you were dead in the trespasses and sins in which you once walked, following the course of this world, following the prince of the power of the air, the spirit that is now at work in the sons of disobedience—among whom we all once lived in the passions of our flesh, carrying out the desires of the body and the mind, and were by nature children of wrath, like the rest of mankind. But God, being rich in mercy, because of the great love with which he loved us, even when we were dead in our trespasses, made us alive together with Christ—by grace you have been saved.
>
> —Ephesians 2:1–5

- Circle the word "dead" and then put brackets around what caused this state and scent of death in our lives.
- Put a box around from whom this deathly scent emanates or starts.
- Underline what kind of children we were and what kind of deeds we did.
- Highlight who moved toward us when we were drenched in the rotten, putrid, stench of death.
- Circle and put a star above what He made us together with Christ.
- Underline the three characteristics of God that changed the scent of death in our lives to life.

Maybe you've never thought about this before, but trespasses, sin, and disobedience to God have a certain, powerful, pungent scent in our lives—the scent of death. You and I were completely incapable of removing that scent from ourselves and choosing life. Everything we did bore this pervasive rotten, deathly scent.

To save us when we could not save ourselves and to change our scent from death to life, God moved toward us in rich mercy, great love, and grace. He braved the horrible scent of our sin, took it upon Himself on the cross, and gave us life. Because of this, the scent and identity of our lives forever changed from being children of wrath to children of God.

Every day, we have a choice. We must choose and keep choosing to move away from the rotten, putrid, dangerous scent of death in which we were steeped and move toward the gracious, merciful, loving scent of life.

The tough thing about the scent of death is that it's often so easy to put on because it's so familiar. It's what we know. It's just like Mia Grace—even though in a moment, she was adopted into our family with the rights and privileges of a new home, a new wardrobe, new opportunities, and privileges of being our daughter, the scent of her orphanage was what she knew. It was a daily choice for her to identify with, choose, and want to move toward the new scent of her new family and new home. As she did so, the old memories were replaced with new ones. The scent of her life slowly but surely transformed from being characterized by fear, pain, abandonment, hurt, independence, and trauma, to trust, beautiful dependence, confidence, courage, and love.

Colossians 2–3 paints a beautiful and vivid picture of this daily choice for us.

Look at Colossians 2:13 below.

"And you, who were dead in your trespasses and the uncircumcision of your flesh, God made alive together with him, having forgiven us all our trespasses."

- Once again, circle the scent of our lives when we were stuck in our trespasses.
- Put a box around the scent God changed our lives to.
- Circle where this life comes from. (Hint: what did God have to do with our trespasses?)

Changing our scent from death to life—from wrath to mercy, love, and grace—begins with forgiveness. That is the scent we must drench in our lives in every day as we move toward living like the children of God.

Read Colossians 3:5–9 in your Bible.

What did Paul say death smells like? What are indicators that death is at work in you in your day-to-day life?

Now go back and read Colossians 3:1–4.

In these verses, Paul reminds us that through the forgiveness of Christ, we have died to sin and who we were in the past. That is no longer to be the scent of our lives. Our scent is now to be characterized by the resurrection. But what does resurrection smell like?

Pick back up with Colossians 3:12–15.

What does a life hidden in the resurrection life of Christ smell like? What are the indicators that life is at work in you in your day-to-day life?

It's humbling, isn't it? Believers in Christ should be the most fragrant, aromatic people on the planet. Our behavior should be so different from all the grudge-holding, argumentative, divisive, angry, offended people around us. Others should be drawn to us, asking us where in the world we get our life-giving, compassionate, kind, humble, patient, forgiving, long-suffering scent. But so much of the time, the scent of our lives is indistinguishable from those who do not know Christ.

I want us to be really honest for a moment. In Colossians 3, look over the two different descriptions of a life drenched in death and a life drenched in Jesus's forgiveness and resurrection life.

Which list most often characterizes your life? What is the scent you most often wear? Explain.

How do you and I become quicker about, stronger in, and more desirous of choosing the scent of life over death? (Hint: Read Colossians 3:16.)

What must dwell in us on a consistent, day-by-day basis for us to wear the scent of Christ?

The Word of God bears the scent of God. Our Bibles don't contain dead words on a page; they contain words of life that have the supernatural power to change our scent. The question for you and me is: Are we wearing it? Are we thinking God's thoughts found in God's Word more than our own? Are we valuing, trusting, and obeying what He says, thinking through all the implications of His commands and righteous rules for our lives? If not, no matter how justified we feel in holding onto our grudges, clutching tightly to our offenses, retorting in angry responses, or slandering and spreading someone's weaknesses, we are living in the stench of death.

But as we learn to release our offenses, let go of our grudges, diffuse our retorts and angry responses, and move towards others in understanding, forgiveness, mercy, and grace, we spread the fragrance of resurrection life.

Is there any specific stench you need to confess and ask forgiveness for today?

Is there a specific scent you would like to put on? If so, what is it? Why?

Close today by writing out a prayer, asking your Father for His help in learning how to bear His scent:

Respond

Father,

When I was dead in my sins and had no power or ability to save myself, You moved toward me, forgave me for all of my offenses, and gave me life through Christ. Please forgive me for holding onto my old scent of death for so long. Choosing life is painful—it requires forgiveness, patience, long-suffering, trust in Your Word, and faithful prayer. But the resurrection life of Christ is the scent I want to bear. Help me to spend the time with You that is needed to instruct my thoughts, form my words, and guide my choices to bear the aroma of eternal life.

DAY 4

Read

Today's Personal Study refers to chapter 18 in the book, "Scent."

Reflect

Today is our last day of working on rebuilding our senses, specifically the sense of scent. Yesterday we processed through the choice we have to turn from wearing the scent of death to putting on the scent of life on a day in and day out basis.

Much of what we thought through had to do with our own choices and actions in choosing resurrection life over sin and death. But what do we do with the lingering scent in our lives from the sin other people have committed against us? What do we do with the scent that our parents, primary caretakers, or often the very people we love or want relationship with the most seem to leave on us—the scent of trauma, abuse, affairs, abandonment, hurt, or betrayal?

Are we doomed to walk around with the defining scent of victim, rejected, unwanted, or betrayed clinging to us for the rest of our lives? Hopefully by this point in the study, you can join me in absolute confidence by saying, "Absolutely not!"

Sin, transgression, and death do not have the final say in our lives. This is the whole point of working toward earned secure attachment. While the effects of sin that we commit and others commit against us are inevitable in this life, a new lens, a new aroma, and a new life is available to us through Christ. As Elisabeth Elliot explains, "The secret is *Christ* in *me*, not me in a different set of circumstances."[31]

One day, our restoration will be complete, and we will have the whole and final picture of the house of living stones Christ is building us into. Until then, we have glimpses only. For now, we see through a mirror, dimly, but one day, one day, we will see Him and all His beautiful, redemptive, restorative purposes for us face to face, with our very own eyes (1 Corinthians 13:12).

Until then, we have a daily choice to make. Like we have talked about before, we must choose to see Jesus. We must choose to sit in His presence and linger long, allowing His robes that are heavy with His restorative scent to envelop us, heal us, and give us comfort, strength, and encouragement. Then we can trade any stench of sin or death we have embraced or that others have flung on us and allow them to be overcome by the only thing in this life that is stronger than death—His resurrection life.

The past seven weeks, we have done a lot of remembering. We have remembered pieces and large chunks of our painful pasts and started to bring them under the restorative, healing touch that only Christ can bring. We've remembered the specifics. Today, let's pause for a moment and think about the overarching scent of our lives. I know that might be an odd thing to consider, but think about it for a moment. When you walk into a room, what is the fragrance, odor, or aroma your life gives off to those around you? Maybe words like victim, lonely, needy, unwanted, heavy-hearted, anxious, weary or chosen, beloved, joyful, peaceful, hopeful, faithful, or encouraging come to mind.

Try to sum up the overarching scent of your life in one word.

Friend, if you are a believer in Christ, there are only two people who get to decide your scent: you and Jesus. That's it. Not you and your parents or you and your best friend. Not you and your spouse or you and your co-workers or you and your teacher from the second grade. That knowledge and assurance carry the possibility and hope of so much life.

Read 2 Corinthians 2:14–16.

As believers in Christ, how often does God lead us in triumphal, victorious procession and through us spread the fragrant aroma of the knowledge of His Son?

Now, look closely at verse 15. Circle the word "are." We are the aroma of Christ. Not some of the time, but all the time.

Think back to the two passages we read yesterday from Ephesians and Colossians: when God rescued you from death and made you alive together with Christ, right then and there He changed your scent permanently and unalterably. For all of eternity, when God looks at you and "smells" you as His child, what He smells and who He smells is Christ.

But we are the ones who daily decide if we will walk in our new aroma and live out our identity as beloved children of God or turn back to our old ways and our old scent as children of wrath (Ephesians 2:3). We can't become children of wrath again, but we can act like it. We can't become dead in our trespasses again, but we can act in ways reminiscent of our old nature. Other people can't reverse or erase the new scent of life God has given us in Christ, but we can choose through unforgiveness or a victim mentality to allow their scent to linger on us.

If you or I have a lingering scent or aroma of death or the deeds of darkness on us, only one thing I know removes it: time spent at the feet of Jesus. It's that simple. Like we have talked about through this study, we have to do the long and intentional work of allowing Him to replace our old memories with new ones of His presence with us in the suffering, trials, pain, or valley. We have to do the work of choosing to put on the new lens of His Word, learning to see all of life through His steadfast love and faithfulness (Psalm 26:3). And we have to sit still, enveloped in His robes, learning what resurrection life and a life lived alongside Him smells like.

I can't tell you exactly what the scent of Christ smells like, but I can sure tell you what it doesn't smell like. It doesn't smell like shame, fear, betrayal, abandonment, or a vague sense of anxiety or depression. It doesn't smell like accusations or a condemning sense of never being enough. I believe it smells something like contentment, peace, satisfaction, trust, joy, and the truth of forgiveness and acceptance despite us, not because of us. In a word, it smells like life.

The longer you walk with Christ and the more time you spend in His presence, treasuring, valuing, and knowing His Word, the faster you will be able to not only identify His scent but want it, long for it, and run from anything that does not usher it in.

Read Luke 4:16–21.

When Jesus began His earthly ministry of healing, teaching, and preparing people's hearts for the kingdom of God, He chose to read a certain portion of Scripture. Where was that portion of Scripture found (v. 17)?

After He read, what did Jesus tell the people in the synagogue?

Now look back at verses 18–19. What exactly had been fulfilled by the life, ministry, and presence of Jesus?

Circle the word "anointed" (v. 18), and then list exactly what the Spirit of the Lord anointed Jesus to do.

To be "anointed" by the Spirit of God is to be set apart by God to do a specific task. In the Old Testament, kings and priests were literally anointed with a certain, special kind of oil made with ingredients that bore a certain scent. That scent represented the empowerment of the Spirit of God to do a certain task.

The implication in Luke 4 is that Jesus's life bore a specific scent—the scent of salvation, freedom, sight, healing, liberty, life, and light—to do a specific task: to save people who could do absolutely nothing to save themselves. His anointing was not to save people from physical enemies or circumstances, but to save people from the ultimate enemy: the stench of sin and death.

Read Isaiah 61:1–4. This is the Scripture Jesus read from that day.
In verse 3, what other elements of Jesus's fragrance do you see?

Now here is the beautiful part: when the Spirit of God, through Christ, changes our aroma—from death to life, from slave to free, from brokenhearted to comforted, from mourning to glad—what do God's people do under the power of Christ's anointing and scent (v. 4)?

Instead of living life as a victim, you become a purposeful rebuilder of ruins. Instead of staying bound as a captive, you become free to help other people restore. Instead of living under the stench of being rejected, unwanted, or brokenhearted, you start living as the restored, remembered, chosen, beloved, wholehearted fragrant son or daughter you were created to be.

Now look back at the beginning of today's personal study at how you described the overarching scent of your life, After reading today's Scriptures, ask yourself: What would I like the signature scent of my life to be?

Jesus spent His whole ministry and life here on this earth telling people one central, amazing thing: Go and sin no more. Go, tell your friends and family what I have done for you. Go, live out your new identity as the chosen, beloved, wanted son or daughter of God.

He told this to adulteresses, prostitutes, women by well-sides, and men in traitorous tax-collector booths. He told this to bleeding, unclean women; leprous men; and dying children. He told this to everyone He encountered who believed He was the Son of God: Don't live out of your old scent. Live out of your new scent. Live with the scent of heaven wrapped around you and the hope of the resurrection enveloping you.

This is my prayer and hope for each one of us as well.

We don't have to live out of our old scent, old lens, old fears, old pain, old traumas, old wounds, and old identities anymore. Through Christ, you are a child of God. Now go and live like one. Earned secure attachment is waiting.

Respond

Father,
Thank You that no one has the power or ability to choose my scent or determine my fragrance except You. I ask for the power, strength, and courage to live out of the anointing, fragrance, and identity that is mine in Christ. As I do so, send me out into a broken world to restore, repair, and rebuild ruins as a beloved child of God.

DAY 5

Read

Today's Personal Study refers to chapter 19 in the book, "Remember, Restore, and Rebuild."

Reflect

Friends, you have traveled so far and done so much incredible work over the past seven weeks. What a journey it has been! You have had to remember the hard things, allow God to restore the broken places, and invite Him into the work of rebuilding a foundation of secure attachment from which you can stand and relate to Him as your good Father for all of your days.

For many of us, this is just the beginning of the journey rather than the end. My journey toward earned secure attachment took many moments of intentional time in God's presence and God's Word, working through old patterns and resentments, letting go of old grudges, getting rid of old lenses, and replacing my old identity with the new. And my journey continues every day, with every choice, and in every season. I am always learning something new about what it means to live like my Father's daughter.

Through my journey, my relationships with my parents, in-laws, husband, children, and friends have grown richer, deeper, and stronger rather than the reverse. There have been many moments of hard, many mornings of working through forgiveness or asking others for forgiveness, and many seasons of learning to receive forgiveness from a Father who offers me His meal of mercy, grace, and goodness every single time I ask.

Read Psalm 120:1.

What did the psalmist do in his distress? What did God do in response?

Now, read Romans 10:9–10.

What must we do to be saved?

While this passage specifically applies to salvation, how might it relate to our fears, worries, and anxieties?

Think back to the very first sense we worked on rebuilding—our hearing. The very first thing a securely attached child does with their parent is cry out. It's that simple: On the days you don't know what to do or where to go, cry out. In the moments when the pain feels like more than you can bear, call out to the Lord. His promise is this: He will answer. He will. Just keep taking the next step, showing up the next day with your Bible, pen, and paper in hand, and cry out to the One who is anointed to save you.

While the road is not always easy, I can promise you this: the presence of Jesus with you in the hard places—His eyes that see you, His hands that steady you, His ears that hear you, His table that nourishes you, His scent that comforts you—far outweighs the memory of any pain or discomfort you might feel. I wouldn't want to walk through specific valleys again, but I wouldn't trade those valleys for any height or mountain peak for the simple reason that those were the places I securely attached to the One who loves me and gave Himself for me. In the days ahead, as you consider Jesus and walk with your Shepherd close by your side, you will be able to look back and say the same thing as well.

For every season of "hard" I have walked through, for every season of fasting from old behaviors and learning to feast on the new, the words of the prophet Isaiah have held out comfort and hope.

Read Isaiah 58:6–12.

While these verses refer to literal fasting from food, God was teaching His people about the heart behind their actions and what their actions in other areas of their lives said about their love for Him. In other words, they were only halfway obedient. So, when they felt like the Lord wasn't hearing them, Isaiah told them how to fast correctly; to change those behaviors and move toward God in obedience. As we move toward earned secure attachment to God, "fasting" from our old behaviors and moving toward Him in love and obedience, God changes us.

As you learn a new way to walk, trust, and obey the Lord, what begins to happen to our places of pain and darkness (vv. 9–10)?

Who do we learn to lean on as our constant guide?

The more dependent, obedient, and trusting we become, what happens to us emotionally, spiritually, and even physically (v. 11)?

What happens to the remembered ruins in our lives (v. 12)?

As God restores and rebuilds us, what do we become and do for others?

What is our new name?

This is how I want to close this study, this workbook, and our time together—with your promised new name. As we stay committed on this journey of intimate dependence and trust and obedience with our good Father, no longer will you and I live out of the ruins of the past or in the mindset of our old identities or attachments. No, we will live in the new. We will join the Lord in His work of remembering, restoring, and rebuilding, and take our place by His side together as the children of God. Restoration is both here and now and is coming in all of its completion. I can't wait to stand in the new heaven and new earth and see it together one day.

> Then I saw a new heaven and a new earth, for the first heaven and first earth had passed away. . . . And I heard a loud voice from the saying, "Behold, the dwelling place of God is with man. He will dwell with them, and they will be his people, and God himself will be with them as their God. He will wipe every tear from their eyes, and death shall be no more, neither shall there be mourning, nor crying, nor pain anymore, for the former things have passed away." And he who was seated on the throne said, "Behold, I am making all things new."
>
> —Revelation 21:1, 3–5

Respond

Father,

Learning to trust You as my heavenly Father will continue to take time, consistency, endurance, and patience. But the process is full of so much joy. Please continue to help me use the tools of Your Word, prayer, the Psalms, and secure, Christ-centered people to tell my story to so I can continue the process of learning to see all my life through a different lens. As Your child, I know You will continue to restore my soul, goodness and mercy will follow me all the days of my life, and I will dwell in Your house forever (Psalm 23:3, 6).

Continuing the Calm

As you move forward in your walk with the Lord, you will face the choice each day to focus on and submit to Him. Do not let previous good choices lull you into thinking you've finally arrived and must not continue seeking the Lord. Do not let previous bad choices move you into a spirit of defeat that keeps you from trying again. Rather, live simply where you are, allowing His grace to wash over you, allowing your eyes to be on His presence and your heart to seek His goodness.

Spend time giving thanks to our Jehovah Jireh, God our Provider. Fully focus on the good He has done for you and provided for you. Breathe in His goodness and exhale the things you need to let go of. Notice them leaving you and let them flow into the hands of the One who is meant to take care of them.

Take these with you as you continue to remember, restore, and rebuild with your Savior. Use any of the skills that have helped you to calm your body and your mind, and seek out others if you need. The journey to healing doesn't stop here. The Lord your God is with you and will be with you wherever you go. We love you and pray for you as you continue beyond this study.

Appendix

REMEMBERING YOUR ATTACHMENT

____

____

Matthew 6:33

GOD

1. ____________________
2. ____________________
3. ____________________

DAD

1. ____________________
2. ____________________
3. ____________________

MOM

1. ____________________
2. ____________________
3. ____________________

SPOUSE OR SIG. OTHER

1. ____________________
2. ____________________
3. ____________________

YOU

CHILDREN

1. ____________________
2. ____________________
3. ____________________

YOUR ATTACHMENT STYLE

____

FRIENDS

1. ____________________
2. ____________________
3. ____________________

1. ____________________
2. ____________________
3. ____________________
4. ____________________

1. ____________________
2. ____________________
3. ____________________
4. ____________________

PSALMS TO USE TO REMEMBER, RESTORE, AND REBUILD FROM INSECURE ATTACHMENT

FOR INSECURE-AMBIVALENT ATTACHMENT:

- For help in healing your inner franticness and deep need for security and stability, use **Psalm 23:1–3.**
- For help in your struggle to find relief from anxiety and deep-seated fear that you will be rejected or abandoned, use **Psalm 23:4–6.**
- For help in placing your needs and neediness before God instead of others, use **Psalm 63:1–3.**
- For help in placing yourself in a position to consistently receive love and know you are never too needy for God to withhold His love, use **Psalm 63:5–8.**
- For help in giving your big emotions a place to go, learning to trust God enough to allow Him to hold your emotions, and waiting on His timing to speak to others, use **Psalm 4:1–5.**
- For help in turning off the loud, persistent voice of self-criticism, self-hatred, and insecurity and learning to hear the quieting, comforting, calming, present, stable, loving, and faithful voice of God, use **Psalm 25:8–10 and Psalm 26:3.**
- For help in freeing yourself from constantly having to seek the approval and reassurance of others, use **Psalm 27:1–3.**
- For help in keeping yourself from pursuing others to have your needs met for security, closeness, approval, and love and reminding yourself that you are God's beloved and the one He pursues, use **Psalm 34:4–6, 8–10.**

FOR INSECURE-AVOIDANT ATTACHMENT:

- For help in being secure enough to risk being known, use **Psalm 139:1–6, 23–24.**
- For help in not feeling shame from your past but to have courage to be honest enough about its impact on you, use **Psalm 51:6.**
- For help in receiving love as a child of God, not for what you do but for who you are, use **Psalm 103:1–5.**
- For help in being honest about hurtful experiences, use **Psalm 31:7.**
- For help in understanding that feeling deeply isn't a weakness, use **Psalm 5:1–3.**
- For help in admitting the past had a big impact on your present but gives you hope for healing and a new kind of future, use **Psalm 119:71–72.**
- For help in learning to be more present to the emotional needs of others, use **Psalm 51:9–13.**
- For help in learning to lean and depend on the safety and security of God's love, use **Psalm 73:25–26.**

LEADER GUIDE

WEEK 1

Read (5 minutes)

- Read Psalm 23:1–6 as an introduction to the study and the next seven weeks.
- Pray for the group, asking God to open hearts and lead each person in the restoration process as their Shepherd and Host at His table.

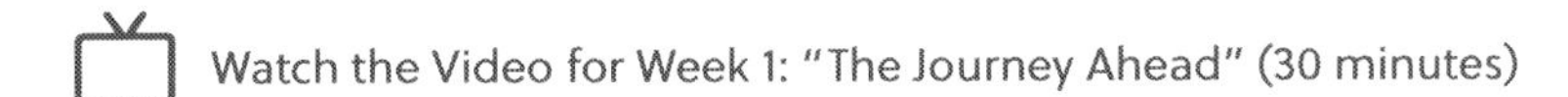

Watch the Video for Week 1: "The Journey Ahead" (30 minutes)

- Remind group members they can take notes in their viewer guide on page 9.

Discuss (30 minutes)

- For the first meeting, take fifteen minutes to:
  - Introduce everyone in your group and encourage people to share what drew them to participate in this study.
  - Talk through your expectations for the study as a leader and ask each group member to share what she hopes to gain from the next seven weeks of remembering and asking God to restore and rebuild.
  - Remind group members to keep what is shared in the group confidential so that over the next seven weeks, your group can be safe space in which members can share, grow, and heal.

- Now for the next fifteen minutes, answer the following questions from this week's video.
  - What about knowing your identity as a sojourner or pilgrim here on this earth is comforting or encouraging?
  - As a pilgrim or sojourner, explain how you have to "untangle your loyalties often."
  - How is it helpful knowing your strength is found on the "highways to Zion"?
  - Allow time for group members who feel comfortable doing so to share one way a desert or a parched or dry place in their lives has become a source of strength.

- Close by discussing how the goal of running toward the presence of God gives you great reward, no matter what your circumstances are like here on this earth.

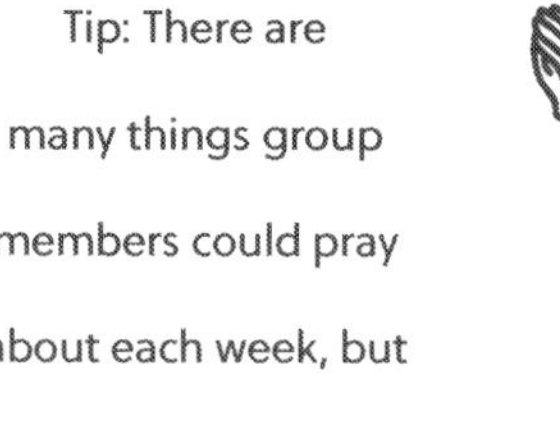

Tip: There are many things group members could pray about each week, but please keep prayer requests limited to one per participant that pertains to their own personal journey of restoration. This will enable everyone to have time to share and help your group remain focused on the topic of the study.

Pray (5 minutes)

- Ask each group member to share one specific way the group can pray for encouragement or strength in their journey toward restoration this week.
- Close by praying the words of Psalm 84:11–12 over your group, thanking the Lord that He is a sun and shield and gives grace, glory, and goodness to His people. Ask for the specific blessing for each group member of learning to trust Him in the journey of restoration ahead.

Read (5 minutes)

- Read 1 Kings 19:11–13 as an introduction to today's session.
- Pray for the group, asking God to open hearts to hear His low whisper and still, small voice as He leads them down the path of remembrance and restoration.

Watch the Video for Week 2: "How God Helps Us Remember" (30 minutes)

- Remind group members they can take notes in their viewer guide on page 35.

Discuss (30 minutes)

- For the first fifteen minutes, discuss questions from last week's personal study:
  - Why is it so important for us to remember rightly?
  - How does remembering God's saving acts in world history and in our own personal history help us remember through a healing lens?

- Think back to Exodus 34:6–8. Does the way you regularly think about and remember God need to change according to who He says He is in His Word? Explain.
- What concepts or questions from last week's study encouraged you?
- What questions from last week's study challenged you?

- Now for the next fifteen minutes, answer the following questions from this week's video.
  - Why does God ask us questions to help us heal?
  - What do God's questions help us identify in our lives?
  - How does God respond to us every time we answer Him honestly?
  - How does this give us hope for the journey of remembering we have ahead?
  - If you feel comfortable doing so, share about one time you chose to remember rightly and one time you chose to remember destructively. How did this choice affect you and the people around you?
  - Close by discussing how choosing to remember rightly can affect everything in your journey of restoration ahead and how your group can be a support to one another.

Pray (5 minutes)

- Ask each group member to share one specific way the group can pray for encouragement or strength in their journey toward restoration this week.
- Close by praying the words of Exodus 34:6–8 over your group, asking the Lord to show each group member who He is and how He never ceases to give the covering of His steadfast love and faithfulness for all who call on His name.

WEEK 3

Read (5 minutes)

- Read Psalm 78:5–7 as an introduction to today's session.
- Pray for the group, asking God to fill their hearts with hope as they remember His Word and the ways He restores us with His mercy, grace, and steadfast love.

 Watch the Video for Week 3: "Restoring Through the Psalms" (30 minutes)

- Remind group members they can take notes in their viewer guide on page 65.

Discuss (30 minutes)

- For the first fifteen minutes, discuss questions from last week's personal study:
  - Look back at Day 2. What are God's two primary acts in world history that set the pattern for us as we remember?
  - According to Psalm 78:44–55 and Ephesians 2:1–10, what do these two acts teach us about how we are to remember anything that happens to us as the children of God?
  - If you feel comfortable doing so, share how you think you were attached to your parents and one or two memories that helped to shape that attachment.
  - Does understanding your attachment style to your parents help to explain your relationships with your spouse, children, friends, or other significant people in your life? Why or why not?
  - How does processing painful moments from your past through the lens of God's Word, specifically Isaiah 43:1–3, help you in the journey of moving toward earned secure attachment?
  - What concepts or questions from last week's study encouraged you?
  - What questions from last week's study challenged you?

- Now for the next fifteen minutes, answer the following questions from this week's video.
  - How does consistent prayer help us to move toward earned secure attachment?
  - How does praying through the Psalms help to restore our souls and move us toward us a place of secure connection with God?
  - Is there one element from Psalm 32 that you want or need to incorporate into your prayer life or the way you relate to God? If so, what is it, and how can it help you move toward earned secure attachment with Him?

 Pray (5 minutes)

- Ask each group member to share one specific way the group can pray for encouragement or strength in their journey toward restoration this week.
- Close by praying the words of Psalm 32:1–7 over your group, asking the Lord to give them the courage to be honest, make Him their hiding place, and hear His shouts of deliverance over every painful memory or hurtful place in their lives.

WEEK 4

 Read (5 minutes)

- Read Psalm 1:1–6 as an introduction to today's session.
- Pray for the group, asking God to open the eyes and ears of their hearts to understand, meditate on, delight in, pray, and live out the truth of His Word, enabling them to flourish in whatever season of life they are experiencing.

 Watch the Video for Week 4: "Restoring Through Prayer" (30 minutes)

- Remind group members they can take notes in their viewer guide on page 97.

 Discuss (30 minutes)

- For the first fifteen minutes, discuss questions from last week's personal study:
  - What are the primary tools God has given us to use to help us move toward earned secure attachment?
  - How does prayer help to restore those who are insecure-avoidantly attached and those who are insecure-ambivalently attached?
  - To create time to tell your story to God through studying His Word and prayer and then to tell your story to others through counseling, mentoring, or friendship, what obstacles in your schedule or life do you need to move? What beliefs in your heart do you need to

examine that keep you from moving forward toward a place of earned secure attachment?
    - Did any of your beliefs about prayer or your relationship with God shift or change this week? Explain.
    - What concepts or questions from last week's study encouraged you?
    - What questions from last week's study challenged you?

- Now for the next fifteen minutes, answer the following questions from this week's video.
    - Why is the concept of adoption so central to understanding our posture in prayer?
    - How does prayer help us work out and live from our identity as the children of God?
    - Go over once again the six things children need from their parents. Were your parents able to meet those six needs in your heart? If not, how can you actively move toward God through the tools He has given you to allow Him to meet those needs?
    - How does knowing God is willing, able, and ready to meet those six needs in you give you hope for the journey ahead?
    - How does knowing your heavenly Father can meet those needs in you enable you to love, forgive, and move toward your earthly parents in honoring, healthy ways?

Pray (5 minutes)

- Ask each group member to share one specific way the group can pray for encouragement or strength in their journey toward restoration this week.
- Close by praying the words of Psalm 139:1–6, 23–24 over your group, asking that the Lord would use time in His Word and prayer to know each one of you, enable you to tell Him your story, and hear Him tell it back to you in a lens of truth, faithfulness, and love. Ask that individual times of regular prayer in the days ahead would meet every need in your hearts and move each one of you toward a place of earned secure attachment with Him.

WEEK 5

 Read (5 minutes)

- Read Psalm 16:5–6 as an introduction to today's session.
- Pray for the group, thanking the Lord that He is their good portion and holds their lives securely in His hands. Ask that He would use His Word in today's session to help their hearts rest securely in His presence as their dwelling place and home.

 Watch the Video for Week 5: "Making God Our Home" (30 minutes)

- Remind group members they can take notes in their viewer guide on page 131.

 Discuss (30 minutes)

- For the first fifteen minutes, discuss questions from last week's personal study:
  - Look back to Day 2 and discuss the definition of a biblical lament. Does knowing that God gives you permission to lament help you in your journey toward earned secure attachment through prayer? Why or why not?
  - Now look back to Day 3. What part of writing your own lament was difficult or hard for you? What part was helpful? Explain.
  - Read Psalm 84:11–12 together. How do these verses give you hope and permission to praise?
  - How can you continue to use both the tools of lament and praise in your journey toward earned secure attachment?
  - What concepts or questions from last week's study encouraged you?
  - What questions from last week's study challenged you?

- Now for the next fifteen minutes, answer the following questions from this week's video.
  - What part or parts of Moses's story or journey toward making God his home that you can relate to or identify with?
  - How do wilderness seasons in our lives help us draw near to God and make Him our secure place?

- When you look back on your life, what helps you see how a wilderness season drew you near to God and shaped or prepared you for what was ahead? Share with your group if you feel comfortable doing so.
- Why is having the margin to hear the voice of God so important in our journey toward making God our home?
- Is there anything or any voice in your life you need to quiet so that you have time, space, or margin to hear God's call and voice in your life?

Pray (5 minutes)

- Ask each group member to share one specific way the group can pray for encouragement or strength in their journey toward restoration this week.
- Close by praying the words of Psalm 90:1–2, 16–17 over your group. Ask God to do whatever it takes to make Himself your secure dwelling place and home. Ask Him to provide each group member with the strength and courage to journey through the wilderness seasons, listen to His voice, and trust His love to keep them secure.

WEEK 6

Read (5 minutes)

- Read Psalm 27:4–5 as an introduction to today's session.
- Pray for the group, asking that the Lord would open the eyes of their hearts to see Him high and lifted up above all earthly things. Pray that the vision they have of Him would transform everything else in their lives, enabling them to walk on a path of secure attachment as His beloved children.

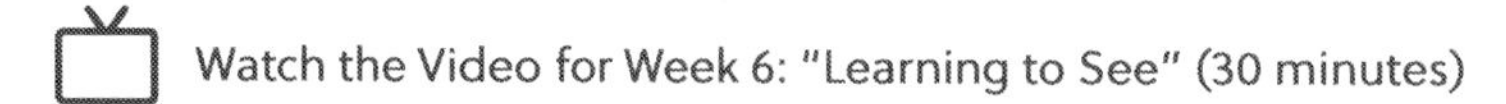

Watch the Video for Week 6: "Learning to See" (30 minutes)

- Remind group members they can take notes in their viewer guide on page 165.

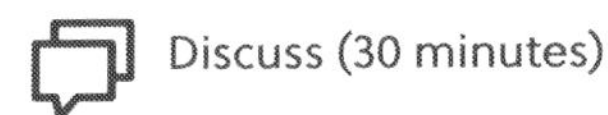

- For the first fifteen minutes, discuss questions from last week's personal study:
  - Read Ephesians 2:1–5 together. Why does rebuilding our spiritual senses play such an important part in our journey toward earned secure attachment with God?
  - Look back at Day 2. How does the sense of hearing play out in a securely attached child? How did you respond and relate to your parents with the sense of hearing? How did the way you learned to relate to them affect the way you relate to God?
  - Look back to Day 3. Why is the work of forgiveness vital in our journey toward earned secure attachment with God?
  - If you feel comfortable doing so, share a way you need help and reminders to forgive those who have hurt you through the years.
  - How does Psalm 34 help us to move toward a place of secure attachment with the Lord?
  - Look back at Day 5. Why is the sense of sight important in building a foundation of secure attachment with your parents and then with the Lord?
  - What concepts or questions from last week's study encouraged you?
  - What questions from last week's study challenged you?

- Now for the next fifteen minutes, answer the following questions from this week's video.
  - What part or parts of Paul's story or journey toward learning to see God can you relate to or identify with?
  - How does seeing Jesus transform and inform everything else in your life?
  - What parts of your life are you still seeing through the worthlessness of the flesh instead of the worthiness of Christ? Explain.
  - How have the weaknesses in your life helped you continue to see Jesus?
  - Is there a weakness you have been rejecting that you need to embrace and see through a different lens to draw near to the sufficiency of Christ? Explain.

- How can you learn to respond to life through the lens of God's love instead of your circumstances?

Pray (5 minutes)

- Ask each group member to share one specific way the group can pray for encouragement or strength in their journey toward restoration this week.
- Close by praying the words of Ephesians 3:14–19 over your group. Ask that the eyes of their hearts would be enlightened to see Jesus and to let that sight transform everything else. Ask that the love of Christ would root and ground them so that they could flourish in the soil where God has planted them, and they would be filled to overflowing with all the fullness of God.

WEEK 7

Read (5 minutes)

- Read Psalm 40:1–3 as an introduction to today's session.
- Pray for the group, thanking the Lord that He is a God of deliverance. Thank Him for the journey of earned secure attachment He invites us all to take and ask that He would continue the journey in each group member today, making their steps secure.

Watch the Video for Week 7: "A Life Restored" (30 minutes)

- Remind group members they can take notes in their viewer guide on page 201.

Discuss (30 minutes)

- For the first fifteen minutes, discuss questions from last week's personal study:
    - Look back at Day 2. How does the sense of touch play out in a securely attached child? How did your parent's touch affect your ability to navigate the world around you physically, emotionally, and relationally?

    - How does God's healing touch help secure and stabilize us physically, emotionally, and relationally?
    - Look back at Day 3. Who are people or what are things you are tempted to lean into apart from God to secure yourself when things around you feel shaken?
    - What seasons has God used in your life to help transfer your stability and security to Him?
    - Look back at Day 5. How does the sense of taste play out in the life of a securely attached child?
    - What meals do you regularly indulge in eating that leave a bitter or unpleasant taste in your mouth?
    - What is the meal at God's table that He is wanting you to sit down to eat and then regularly share with others?
    - What concepts or questions from last week's study encouraged you?
    - What questions from last week's study challenged you?

- Now for the next fifteen minutes, answer the following questions from this week's video.
    - What part(s) of Jacob's story or journey toward making God His secure place can you relate to or identify with?
    - Like Jacob, what fears do you need to be delivered from in your journey toward earned secure attachment?
    - What does a healthy fear of God do for our souls?
    - How does honesty and transparency before God enable us to receive true blessing?
    - What does true blessing from God look like? Is that a blessing you are actively moving toward? If not, why not? How can you begin to do so and remember to continue doing so in the days ahead?

 Pray (5 minutes)

- Ask each group member to share one specific way the group can continue to pray for them in the days ahead as they continue their journey toward earned secure attachment with God.
- Close by praying the words of Numbers 6:24–26 over your group. Thank the Lord for all He has done in their lives to move them toward a place of earned secure attachment with Him. Ask that He would continue to

do the good work of securing their hearts in His blessing, presence, favor, and peace through every season and leg of the journey in the days ahead. Thank Him for always being a good Father who helps us remember, restore, and rebuild.

OPTIONAL FINAL GROUP SESSION:

If you group would like to meet for a final time to discuss the last week of personal study, please feel free to schedule one last group meeting to do so.

You can:

- Read and pray Psalm 23:1–6 over your group one last time.
- Discuss concepts or questions from last week's study that encouraged and challenged you.
- Celebrate the ways God has healed and restored you over the last seven weeks.
- Share the steps you want to put in place to continue the journey of earned secure attachment ahead.
- Pray for one another to have courage, strength, and endurance in the journey ahead, trusting that God will give each of you exactly what you need to rebuild a life standing securely on His faithfulness and love.

VIDEO SESSION ANSWERS (IN ORDER OF OCCURRENCE):

Week 1

Identity, pilgrims, on the way, loyalties, often, person, God, family, home, Strength, degree, highways, Zion, dryness, desert, descend, goal, toward

Week 2

where, why, what, lies, where, forgiven, healed, restored, God, lies, who, where, why, looking, hearts, consequences, just, covering, merciful, hope, deliverance, hiding, destructively, rightly, everything

Week 3

story, listener, lens, details, life, Father, heaven, solitude, Word, prayer, Word, God, relationship, covering, honesty, repentance, refuge, intimacy, trust, love

Week 4

Father, adoption, posture, identity, dependent, connected, securely attached, attunement, responsiveness, engagement, regulate, negative, repair, earthly, heavenly, Him

Week 5

You, You, God, home, waters, presence, sins, presence, wilderness, margin, well, presence, guidance, friendship, wisdom, humble, dependent, voice, God, hear, attuned, responsive

Week 6

cannot, receive, gradually, transforms, informs, worthlessness, worthiness, weaknesses, continue, comprehend, love, circumstances, love

Week 7

from, himself, never, less, left, pretend, blessing, to, God, opens, expands, restores, remember, blessing, revelation, invoked, involved

SOURCES

1 *Zondervan NASB Exhaustive Concordance* (Grand Rapids, Michigan: Zondervan, 2000), 1460.

2 Gregg Jantz, "Four Attachment Styles in Relationships Dependency," The Center: A Place of Hope, September 4, 2016, https://www.aplaceofhope.com/four-attachment-styles-in-relationships-dependency. Used by permission.

3 Miroslav Volf, *The End of Memory: Remembering Rightly in a Violent World* (Grand Rapids, MI: Wm. B. Eerdmans Publishing Co., 2006), 10.

4 Timothy Keller, *The Songs of Jesus: A Year of Daily Devotions in the Psalms* (New York: Viking, 2015), 253.

5 Derek Kidner, *Psalms 73-150* (Downers Grove, IL: InterVarsity Press, 2014), 512.

6 Dane Ortlund, *Gentle and Lowly: The Heart of Christ for Sinners and Sufferers* (Wheato, IL: Crossway, 2020), 146.

7 Ibid., 151-152.

8 Ibid., 150.

9 "The Attributes of God - Study Resources," Blue Letter Bible, accessed November 11, 2021, https://www.blueletterbible.org/faq/attributes.cfm.

10 Volf, *The End of Memory*, 103.

11 Volf, *The End of Memory*, 109.

12 Volf, *The End of Memory*, 79-80.

13 Gregg Jantz, "Four Attachment Styles"

14 Curt Thompson, *Anatomy of the Soul: Surprising Connections between Neuroscience and Spiritual Practices That Can Transform Your Life and Relationships* (Carol Stream, IL: Tyndale House, 2010), 115-116.

15 Keller, *The Songs of Jesus*, 1.

16 Annie Dillard, *The Writing Life* (New York: HarperPerennial, 1990), 32.

17 Warren Baker, D.R. E., ed., *Hebrew-Greek Key Word Study Bible: English Standard Version* (Chattanooga, TN: AMG Publishers, 2013), #1485, 2097.

18 These six needs are taken from Adam Young's article, "The Big Six: What Every Child Needs from Their Parents," found at adamyoungcounseling.com/free-documents.

19 Kidner, *Psalms 73-150*, 338.

20 Ibid.

21 Alec Motyer, *Psalms by the Day: A New Devotional Translation* (Scotland: Christian Focus Publications, 2016), 237.

22 Keller, *The Songs of Jesus*, 317.

23 Spiros Zodhiates and Warren Patrick Baker, eds., *Hebrew-Greek Key Word Study Bible: New American Standard Bible* (Chattanooga, TN: AMG Publishers, 1990), 1731.

24 Henri J.M. Nouwen, *Life of the Beloved* (New York: The Crossroad Publishing Company, 1992), 44-46.

25 Elisabeth Elliot, *Keep a Quiet Heart* (Grand Rapids, MI: Revell, 1995), 57.

26 C.S. Lewis, *Mere Christianity* (New York: HarperOne, 1952), 205.

27 Kenneth E. Bailey, *The Good Shepherd: A Thousand-Year Journey from Psalm 23 to the New Testament* (Downers Grove, IL: InterVarsity Press, 2014), 38.

28 Sam Hughey, "Letters of John Newton: The Reformed Reader," Letters of John Newton | The Reformed Reader, accessed October 26, 2021, http://www.reformedreader.org/rbb/newton/letter04.htm.

29 Ibid.

30 Warren Baker, D.R. E., ed., *Hebrew-Greek Key Word Study Bible: English Standard Version* (Chattanooga, TN: AMG Publishers, 2013), #1967, 2128.

31 Elliot, *Keep a Quiet Heart*, 20.

ABOUT THE AUTHOR

SUSANNAH BAKER is a writer, Bible study teacher, and founder of Restore Retreats for women. She graduated from Texas A&M University with a Bachelor of Arts in English. Since graduation, Susannah has written and taught Bible studies for women for over twenty years including *Waiting on the Lord*, *Known*, and *Secure: Connecting to God Through Persistent Prayer.* Through the different tools of her teaching, blogging, Bible studies, prayer guides, and retreats, Susannah loves to help people restore and rebuild secure connection with God.

Apart from Jesus Christ, her greatest loves are her husband of twenty years, Jason, and her four beautiful daughters. Most days you can find her at home with her family in Houston, Texas, praying, writing, and talking about how to restore through relationship with Jesus Christ. She loves to connect with people over coffee, a run, or a hike in the mountains whenever she gets the chance for an adventure.

Connect with her about daily life on her blog, download the free resources she loves to write for people to use in their own journey of healing, view her speaking schedule, or follow her on social media.

WWW.SUSANNAHBAKER.COM

Click on "Speaking" to see Susannah's teaching schedule and inquire about having her speak at your event or to your podcast audience.

Instagram
@baker.susannah

FREE TOOLS TO HELP YOU RESTORE

REMEMBER AND REBUILD: A GUIDE TO PRAYING THROUGH THE PAST

To help you pray through hard memories from your past or difficult situations in your present, download this free tool to give you prompts to process, pray, and heal through God's Word.

Download your free copy at
susannahbaker.com/free-tools

RESTORE THROUGH LAMENT: A GUIDE TO WRITING YOUR OWN LAMENT

Sometimes we have buried hurts so deeply or become so accustomed to holding our emotions in instead of processing them before our holy, good, listening God that we need help knowing how to lament. Download this free tool to give you the same prompts from the workbook to help you remember, grieve, process, and pray.

Download your free copy at
susannahbaker.com/free-tools

DON'T MISS THE COMPANION BOOK TO THE BIBLE STUDY

My adopted daughter and I have different backgrounds, histories, and stories, but the same fear of abandonment and rejection plagued us both. *Restore: Remembering Life's Hurts with the God Who Rebuilds* is our story and journey toward healing. The book helps to identify tools of restoration and the way to rebuild one step at a time. It doesn't take a counseling degree or a course in graduate school to learn how to use them; it simply takes desire, time, focus, and endurance. It takes trust and a willing heart to learn how to receive your heavenly Father's love. Restoration is waiting.

Available online at www.susannahbaker.com/biblestudies or Amazon.

A WEEKEND AWAY TO RESTORE

So many things happen to us over the course of a year and over the course of a lifetime. But we rarely slow down and create intentional time and space for God to help us remember the past, restore our souls, and invite us into His good story for the present and future.

Out of this desire to allow people to have an extended amount of time to remember, restore, and rebuild, our Restore Team created a weekend retreat to do exactly this.

Over the course of the weekend, participants will worship, listen to personal testimonies, and hear solid biblical teaching. There will also be time for quiet and solitude with guided questions and heart-work after each teaching session as well as time to enjoy a beautiful retreat setting with other participants.

If you would like more information about these retreats and when they will occur, please visit www.susannahbaker.com/retreats.

RESTORATION HAPPENS WHEN WE WAIT.

Waiting isn't deprivation. It's your invitation to relationship with God and restored life. In this nine session Bible study, find out how to heal in all of life's waits.

Each study includes:

- 9 FREE Supplemental Teachings
- 8 weeks of Personal Study
- Questions to use in a small group setting

Available online at www.susannahbaker.com/biblestudies, Amazon, or Barnes & Noble.